ELECTRIC

Martin Roundell Greene

First published in Great Britain in 2006
by Martin Roundell Greene
Fern House, Seaborough Road, Henley, Crewkerne TA18 8PJ
www.clarityenglish.co.uk   books@clarityenglish.co.uk

ISBN 10   0-9552675-0-1
ISBN 13   978-0-9552675-0-5

Printed by Creeds the Printers, Broadoak, Bridport DT6 5NL. Tel: 01308 423411

ACKNOWLEDGEMENTS

The research and editing of *Electric Lyme* could not have been completed without the generous help of many people. In particular I would like to thank most sincerely the following for their contributions:

The *Bridport News*, the patient staff at the Dorset County Records Office, Ian Dicks, Jo Draper and her colleagues at the Lyme Regis Museum, Philip Evans, Jenefer and Andrew Farncombe, Ken Gollop, Miles Goslett, Alan Graham, John Hanson, David Hood, Michael Humphries, Peter Lamb and the South West Electricity Historical Society, Roger Mayne, Sir David Mostyn, Noel Osborne, Roz Price, Holly Robinson, Judy Simmonds, Fred Thompson, Christian Tyler, Lilly Wareham (nee Collier), and Western Power Distribution.

Special thanks to Dick Hitchcock for his time and clear memory. It was his remark, 'You know, we used to turn the street-lamps off on moonlit nights to save money' that sparked my interest in the subject.

Leslie Hannah's *Electricity Before Nationalisation* (1979 The Macmillan Press) cleared much technical fog, as did *The Willing Servants* by Anthony Byers (1981 The Electricity Council) and *Electric Universe* by David Bodanis (Little, Brown 2005).

I am most grateful to the following for their kind permission to reproduce photographs and other images from their collections. I have attempted to identify all the copyright owners. If, however, the copyright of any of these images belongs to someone other than those listed below, I apologise for the infringement and would ask the copyright owner, please, to make contact with me so that I can acknowledge the correct ownership in any subsequent printings of this book. Other images and charts are from my own collection. Page-numbers follow the acknowledgement.

Amberley Working Museum: 120; Anne, Countess Attlee: 165; Nick Baldwin: 63; General Peter Benson: 144; Roger Bird: 115; Dennis Bowditch: 167, the Bridport News: 89, 137, 138, 139, 146, 147, 151, 158; 163; Alexander Dennis Ltd: 102; Ian Dicks: 2, 4, 44, 152 and the front and back cover designs and the Electric Lyme logo designs; Dorset County Council Library Service: 5, 15, 20, 56, 59, 95, 114, 131, 143; Dorset History Centre: 57, 32; George Eyre: 77,112, 117; Bob Fowler: 54; John and Sarah Fowles: 34; Gilbert Gilkes & Gordon Ltd: 22; Ken Gollop: 157; Miles Goslett: 12; Alan Graham: 119; Guernsey Electricity Ltd: 168; John Hanson: 48, 162; Tony Hillman: 73, 75; Dick Hitchcock: 7,13, 16, 24, 29, 60, 76, 93, 114, 129;140, 141; 150, 168; Michael Humphries: 142 and 170; the Imperial War Museum, London: 134; the Institution of Electrical Engineers: 64; the Lyme Regis Museum: 6, 14, 17,18, 21, 23, 25, 26, 30, 32, 33, 35, 36, 38, 48, 52, 67, 69, 78, 80, 83, 88, 122, 164; Sir David Mostyn: 32 and 39; Guy Ravenscroft: 90; Carol Reid: 156; Judy Simmonds: 57; Virgil Turner: 71; Roger Vaughan: back cover ladies; Lilly Wareham (nee Collier): 110 and 126; Keith Wiscombe: 161; the Woodroffe School: 10.

The maps on page iii and page 31 are adapted from the Ordnance Survey Map of Lyme Regis of 1905. The images on pages 9 and 55 are reproduced from the Lyme Regis Borough Collection (ref DC/LR) stored at the Dorset History Centre. The copyright of the document shown on page 9 belongs to, and is reproduced courtesy of, Lyme Regis Town Council.

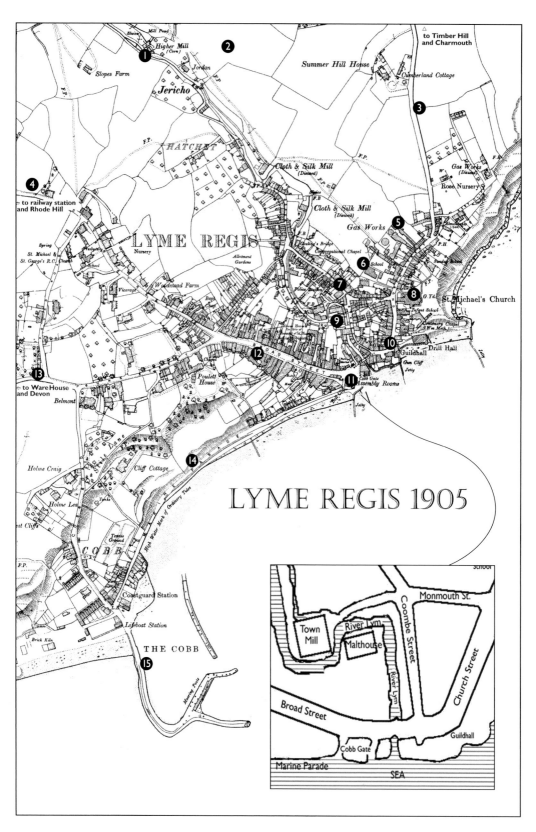

LYME REGIS 1905

to Timber Hill
and Charmouth

Summer Hill House

Cumberland Cottage

Gas Works
(Disused)

Rose Nursery

Gas Works

to railway station
and Rhode Hill

Spring

St. Michael &
St. George's R.C. Church

LYME REGIS

Nursery

Vicarage

Allotment
Gardens

Woodmead Farm

Cloth & Silk Mill
(Disused)

Cloth & Silk Mill
(Disused)

Goslin's Bridge

Congregational Chapel

School

St. Michael's Church

Guildhall

Drill Hall

Gun Cliff
Jetty

Cobb Gate
Assembly Rooms

Jetty

Poulett
House

to Ware House
and Devon

Belmont

Holme Craig

Cliff Cottage

Holme Lea

High Water Mark of Ordinary Tides

West Cliffs

Tennis
Ground

COBB

Coastguard Station

Lifeboat Station

Brick Kiln

THE COBB

Higher Mill
(Corn)

Sluice

Mill Pond

Jordan

Slopes Farm

Jericho

HATCHET

School

Monmouth St.

Town
Mill

River Lym

Malthouse

Coombe Street

River Lym

Church Street

Broad Street

Cobb Gate

Guildhall

Marine Parade

SEA

LYME REGIS 1905

1 Higher Mill
2 Colway Mead
3 Road to Charmouth
4 Road to Railway Station
   and Uplyme
5 Gas Works
6 National School
7 Coombe Street
8 Parish Church
9 Malthouse & Town Mill
10 Guildhall
11 Cobb Gate & Assembly Rooms
12 Broad Street
13 To Ware House
14 Marine Parade
15 Cobb

Dedicated
to my darling
wife Jo

CONTENTS

INTRODUCTION

E*lectric Lyme* is the story of a little English town getting to grips with the twentieth century. It begins in a horse-drawn gas-lit age of gentlemen and servants. On 1st June 1909 Mayor Sam Harris switched a golden switch and 'the new illuminant' appeared in the streets of the town. The large crowd 'cheered lustily' and then sang *God Save the King*. Lyme Regis had become the first town in Dorset with electricity.

Forty years later the story ends in the brave new world of the post-war Welfare State. On the eve of electricity nationalisation, the council held a farewell dinner for its electricity workers at *The Three Cups Hotel*. From tomorrow they would belong to SWEB. In between lie social and technical revolutions, the Depression and two world wars.

The thread that holds *Electric Lyme* together is the spread of the town's own home-made electricity supply. The bigger picture is a civic and social history. It includes stately homes and slums, the workhouse and the waterworks, municipal pride and the municipal dump. The mayor doles out rough justice (chastisement for the young, hard labour for others), the council finds work for the unemployed ('preference to be given to married men'), and the medical officer of health reports on illegitimacy, flushing lavatories, eugenic sterilisation of the mentally unfit and flowers in council house gardens. There is patriotism, skulduggery and, if you look hard enough, even a hint of sex.

Through all this runs the steady spread of electricity. First a few telephones and dim, unreliable lights appear: expensive lamps in expensive homes and streetlights turned off when the moon is bright to save the ratepayers' pennies. Then the cinema, wireless and electric iron arrive. Cars now have compulsory rear lights and electric windscreen wipers. Ordinary families are gradually persuaded to connect up. On the horizon are council houses, built ready-wired for electricity. The chairman of the council's electricity committee acquires the first privately-owned fridge in town. In newspapers there are advertisements for electric washing machines and wedding presents.

Electric Lyme is the story of our grandparents' generation: their values and changing lives; how they lived and thought. It is also the largely untold story of how electricity – that silent servant on which now we entirely depend – arrived in our lives

The fact that *Electric Lyme* is set in Lyme Regis is pure chance. With variations, the same tale unfolded in a thousand other towns across the land.

CREATIVE SPARKS

It is a truth universally acknowledged that all technology starts life as a curiosity, is then taken for granted and finally passes largely unremarked. In its early years the new technology usually costs a lot and is often dangerous. Think of the printing press, New York, the pop-up toaster. And the people who develop it are generally regarded as slightly batty but mainly harmless.

The history of electricity is thankfully short. In the 17th and 18th centuries a few gentleman-scientists began to apply their minds to the subject and conduct electrical experiments. You could generate static electricity with frictional machines and shock your friends. Benjamin Franklin flew a kite in a thunderstorm to see whether lightning had anything to do with electricity, and failed to kill either his son or himself.

But at the start of the nineteenth century things began to get serious. The name of Count Alessandro Volta who invented the first battery was immortalised in the 'volt'. Other scientists and inventors had their names likewise honoured, attached to other electrical units or discoveries: James Watt, André Marie Ampère, Heinrich Hertz, George Ohm, Luigi Galvani & James Joule.

Probably the greatest breakthrough came in 1821 when Michael Faraday demonstrated the principle of the electric motor and, ten years later, showed how to turn it round to become a generator. The discovery was crucial: it showed you could change electricity into mechanical power and mechanical power into electricity. Soon the first small generators were on sale.

The move from experiments to the practical use of electricity came in 1844 when Samuel Morse with his telegraph linked Baltimore with Washington DC. Then in 1857 the world's first practical electric light, an arc light, was installed in the lighthouse in Dungeness. By the end of the 1870s, Alexander Graham Bell had made the first telephone call from Brown's Hotel in London and arc-lights were being used to illuminate Blackpool's seafront, London's Gaiety Theatre, a football stadium in Sheffield and an ironworks near Derby.

The trouble with arc-lights, however, is that their light – formed by an electric arc between two carbon rods – is intensely bright, often flickering and usually smelly. They also need regular adjusting. Because of this, the committee reporting in 1878 to the main London gas company on the threat from electricity said it was 'quite satisfied that electric light can never be applied indoors'.

1 CREATIVE SPARKS

It spoke too soon. On 18th December that year Sir Joseph Swan, a prosperous self-educated chemist and inventor from Newcastle, demonstrated the world's first 'incandescent lamp': what we today call a light bulb. Edison's independent invention in the USA was not patented until a year later. In 1882, the two buried their differences and formed the Edison & Swan United Electric Light Co to install lighting systems and supply light bulbs to the rich and famous.

In 1880 Swan lit the picture gallery in his own home in Gateshead with the new lighting, and in December the shipbuilding magnate Sir William Armstrong installed Swan lamps in his house near Newcastle, using a water turbine to drive a dynamo. The House of Commons, Savoy Theatre, British Museum and Royal Academy installed their first electric lights the following year.

In private homes, the incandescent lamp became a status symbol. To start with, as there was no public electricity supply, expensive generators needed to be installed in each customer's house. But the advantages of the new lamp were immediately obvious. It was small and gave a steady light. More importantly, while all other forms of lighting needed constant attention, the electric lamp was there at just the flick of a switch. It was also much less of a fire risk, and last but not least it was clean.

It was this cleanliness that in time revolutionised interior decoration. The reason for Victorian dark paints and wallpapers was not mere fashion. Until Swan's lamp, all forms of lighting produced smoke so decoration had to cope with its stains. The electric bulb made a whole new world of pale paints and wall-papers possible.

The world's first electric street lighting appeared in Godalming in Surrey in 1881. These were arc-lights with current from a water-powered system, installed and operated by the German company Siemens. Next January, Thomas Edison opened the first steam-driven power station in London's Holborn to light incandescent street lamps. Brighton followed in February and holds the record for the longest unbroken public supply in the world. The original Godalming and Holborn supplies were short-lived. Only when his Pearl Street power-station opened in September 1882 did Edison turn electric lights on in New York, with a flourish, at the offices of his wealthiest customer, the banker J.Pierpoint Morgan.

In the early days, clanking steam engines drove most of the larger power stations. Smaller generators had oil or gas engines. However, for producing electricity, all these engines suffer from a built-in mechanical inefficiency: they work by pistons going up and down while you generate electricity with magnets or conductors whizzing round and round. Converting the one motion into the other wastes energy.

The solution was a rotary turbine. The water turbine, a highly developed sort of horizontal waterwheel, already existed. Then in 1884 the younger son of the 3rd Earl of Rosse, Charles Parsons, took out his first patent on a steam turbine and in 1888 successfully installed the first production model in a power station in Newcastle. Within 25 years, virtually all new generators in major public supply systems – but not Lyme Regis - were driven by steam turbines. Compared with piston-driven engines, for each kilowatt they generated, their fuel consumption was nearly 70 per cent less.

For the last 20 years of the Victorian Age, other uses for electricity began to develop – electric trams and electric lifts, bells, telephones and the electric chair – but by far its most important use was for lighting. There were still few public supply companies so a lot of electricity was 'home-made', with small generators driven by oil engines or water turbines.

Gradually, public electricity supplies appeared in the more prosperous districts of London and go-ahead provincial cities. Sheffield and Taunton were among the first in 1886, Bournemouth (then in Hampshire) in 1888 and Bristol in 1893. Other cities were slower: Southampton waited until 1896 and Plymouth until 1899.

But slow takes on an entirely new meaning when we come to Dorset. Although a few modest private schemes existed, Sherborne and Blandford did not have public supplies of electricity until 1912 and Dorchester, the county town, waited until 1913. Pride of place, though, is earned by Bridport, the next town along the coast to the east of Lyme Regis. At the start of 1926 the mayor told the council that on the subject of electricity Bridport had 'stood aloof for too long and must now march with other towns and boroughs by making use of that power'. The council agreed but then had second thoughts. The town's public electricity supply did not finally commence until 21st December 1929.

Even by 1929, for most of the rural population in south-west England electricity was still decades away. At nationalisation in 1948, the new South West Electricity Board reported that only 20 per cent of the 35,000 farms and smallholdings in their area had a supply, and only 8 per cent were using electricity for any purpose other than lighting.

Back in 1909, its arrival in Lyme Regis made the town the first in Dorset with a public electricity supply, and put it among the most up-to-date in south-west England.

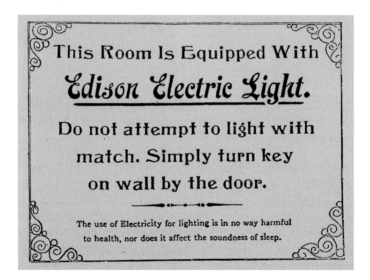

This Room Is Equipped With

Edison Electric Light.

Do not attempt to light with match. Simply turn key on wall by the door.

The use of Electricity for lighting is in no way harmful to health, nor does it affect the soundness of sleep.

PREPARATIONS

L yme Regis is in Dorset. The little River Lym rises in the hills around, then rushes down through the heart of the town to meet the sea. For a thousand years the people have used the river to water and flush their town, its power to drive their mills and its course as a route inland. But the reason for Lyme's existence is the sea.

Thanks to the famous Cobb, Lyme Regis offers the only half-safe anchorage in the English Channel between Weymouth to the east and Dartmouth to the west. In medieval times it was one of the south coast's principal ports. 'Wool out, wine in' summed up its trade. That and fish. And a royal charter from Edward III gave Lyme a borough status, the right to send two members to sit in Parliament and the Regis part of its name.

Goods from the harbour at the Cobb would make their way east along the sea-front to the mouth of the River Lym, and then onto pack-horses to plod up Coombe Street away from the sea, eventually to link with the old road from Dorchester to Exeter and beyond. Coombe Street with its crowded houses, shops and inns, was the heart of the medieval town. And it was in and around Coombe Street four hundred years later that electricity first appeared in Lyme.

———————•———————

By the 1890s Lyme Regis was refined. For more than a century it had attracted genteel visitors who built themselves elegant villas and romantic cottages on the hillsides above the old town. There were cards and balls in the Assembly Rooms, sea air and bathing machines, and gossip and snobbery and the afternoon promenade along the Cobb. In 1859 the *Post*

The Assembly Rooms (left) and Victoria Hall at Cobb Gate were demolished in 1929 to make way for a more profitable car park. The Gate, used by Customs to control access to the cart road to the Cobb, stood on the right.

Office Directory described the streets as 'lighted by gas and well paved'. The town even had its own literary journal called *The Grove*, but no railway. And at least one contributor to *The Grove* was anxious not to have one.

In an article in 1891 entitled 'Why should not Lyme have the electric light?', one A.R.Sharpe argued that as Taunton was 'blessed with the electric light, why should Lyme be behind?' And for those unfamiliar with electricity he enthused, 'All the [street] lamps can be simultaneously lit from the central office. The electric light does not require a man to go round to each lamp to light it and put it out'. But in the same article Mr Sharpe warned against bringing the railway to the town.

A railway would bring 'trippers', and trippers would drive away the summer visitors who 'enliven this town where the tired Londoner can hear what the wild waves are saying without the accompaniment of a barrel organ obligato.' And whilst the nicer class of visitor would 'be drawn to Lyme by a good electric light, as moths are drawn to a candle', a railway would encourage entirely the wrong sort. In any case, Mr Sharpe concluded, 'many who do not have carriages of their own would prefer the exhilaration of a ride in the omnibus to a stuffy railway journey'. The omnibus he was referring to ran on hay and oats. The first practical petrol-driven car, the three-wheeled Benz Motorwagen, had only clattered into life six years before, and was still some way off from Lyme Regis.

In 1903, however, despite Mr Sharpe's dire warning, the cuttings were cut, the embankments embanked, a viaduct thrown across the Cannington Valley and the trains from Axminster arrived. Soon in the summer holidays, the railway was bringing 2,000 trippers and similar disreputable persons to Lyme every day. But still no electricity, or at least no public supply.

The first train arrived in Lyme Regis in summer 1903.

In 1908 Lyme Regis Borough Council was powerful. The councillors and aldermen - four venerable councillors who no longer needed to go through the tedious business of regular re-election - were usually local tradesmen, often from local families and always men. Women would have to wait until after the war to end all wars to be trusted with the vote.

2 PREPARATIONS

The names of Lyme's council committees of the period give a flavour of its attitudes and priorities. There was the School Attendance Committee, the Highways and Sanitation Committee, the Horse Committee, the Watch (as in night watchmen: 'It's three o'clock and all's well. Sorry, did I wake you up?') and Light Committee, the Almshouses Committee and the Burial Board.

The first evidence of any electricity in Lyme appeared in January 1908. The General Post Office wrote to the borough council on the subject of telephones. Would Lyme and neighbouring Charmouth like the GPO 'to arrange telephone communication with the rest of the country by means of a line run from Bridport'? In order to connect, the two parishes would have to guarantee a contribution of up to £15 13s.4d.* a year towards the costs. As there was no mains supply yet, the telephone system must have been powered by battery cells, with callers wildly cranking little handles and shouting into wall-mounted mouth-pieces, 'Hullo? Operator? Hullo! Confound it, Mildred! I tell you there's nobody there. Operator! Operator!'

In March the council agreed to erect Lyme's first traffic sign. It was a notice near the National School opposite the parish church telling motorists to slow down so as not to run over the children. Those were the days when children still expected to play in the streets. At the same meeting the council rejected by one vote a motion to limit the working time of horses in the town to eight hours a day.

Mr Wallis's Lyme Regis Gas & Range Co works in the early 1900s.

In June 1908 the council renewed its street-lighting contract with the Lyme Regis Gas & Range Co for, as it turned out, the last time. The extraordinary feature of the contract was that the company was not required to light the street lamps for six nights each month 'on or around each full moon'. This was one lamp-free night more than in 1907, perhaps as a cost-cutting exercise. If cloud required the lamps to be lit on additional nights, then the company would charge extra. The agreed cost to the council for providing it with the 75 gas streetlamps was £240, or £3 4s.0d. per lamp per year.

* See under Money in chapter *25 Postscripts* for notes on the old system of pounds, shillings and pence.

2 PREPARATIONS

At the end of August the council gave a Mr Chalmers permission to lay a short underground electric cable across Stile Lane 'at a depth of about a foot', on condition that he promised to dig it up again if asked. Probably Mr Chalmers or his neighbour had installed a private generator in one of the substantial houses flanking the lane and wanted to share the current.

At the same meeting councillors passed a motion expressing sympathy to the family of Mr James Tisdall Woodroffe of the Ware Estate, who had died. James, a former Advocate General of Bengal, had bought the estate in 1898. His son Alban will play an important role in this story. In his will James bequeathed a small plot of land off Coombe Street, the site of the medieval *George Hotel*, to the people of Lyme 'in perpetuity for their leisure and recreation'. Today this is George's Square, the garden where Lyme's war memorial stands.

George's Square, known to locals as 'Cats Park', in the heart of the town. A Saxon settlement probably covered this site.

On 15th December the council agreed to meet an electrical engineer, Mr Charles Balbiani, the following evening to give him an opportunity to explain a scheme he had to light the town with electricity. At a special meeting after Christmas, councillors voted to adopt his scheme and also, to put all this modernisation in perspective, to accept a contribution of £20 from Mrs Paine of Temple House for the erection of a drinking trough for horses.

The Lyme Regis and Charmouth telephone exchange opened on 30th December 1908. According to the Telephone Directory for Southern England (1909), there were just seven subscribers: the Lyme and Charmouth Post Offices, the Alexandra Hotel, H.& T.Foxwell (Decorators, Glaziers and Plumbers), E.A.Ffooks Esq of a fine stone house on the seafront called The Sundial, A.D.Pass of Wootton Fitzpaine Manor and Alban Woodroffe up at Ware House. The stage was now set for the arrival of electricity.

3
THE START

O n Thursday evening 16th December 1908 snow was falling as Engineer Carlo Balbiani
made his way down Broad Street towards the Guildhall. If you listened hard you could
hear the hiss of the gas lamps, and of the great snowflakes as they hit their hot iron tops, and
from beyond Cobb Gate the rhythmic hiss of the sea. But Engineer Balbiani was not listening:
at six o'clock he was invited to present to the Watch & Light Committee of Lyme Regis
Borough Council his plan to bring the electric light to the town. If they agreed, fame and
fortune surely lay ahead. Carlo paused, drew himself up to his full if slightly disappointing
height, flung out an arm and started to sing.

In fact, according to the Met Office the weather in Lyme that day was unusually mild
(max.55°F, 13°C) with some sunshine (2.7 hours) and a south-south-westerly wind, Beaufort
Force 3 (approx.9 kts). So much for the snow. Also, none of the documents give Engineer
C. Balbiani's first name as Carlo. It just sounds better than Charles. But we can be sure that
the streets were lit by gas that night because the council's contract with the Lyme Regis Gas
& Range Co stipulated that they should be (except for six nights each month 'on or around
the full moon'), and on 16th December 1908 only 36 per cent of the face of the moon was
illuminated. The lamplighter would have been doing his round.

The minutes of Lyme Regis Borough Council meetings are recorded in firm black
handwriting on ruled pages in heavy leather-bound books. If you want to see them today
you go to the County Records Office in Dorchester where they frisk you for pens and sweets,
sell you a pencil and send you off to wait at a numbered table, equipped with an oversized
pillow. You can snooze on this while they rummage around for the documents you want, but
its official purpose is to support, when it eventually arrives, the ancient book so that its spine
is not damaged. If you lick your fingers when turning its pages, someone will come along and
smack you on the wrist.

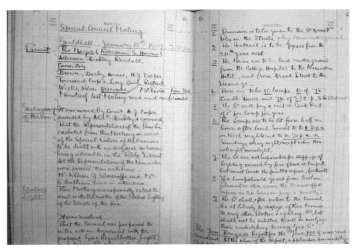

Borough Council minutes recording the original agreement with the Electric Light Co, 18th January 1909.

3 THE START

The lead-up to Engineer Balbiani's electric presentation is unknown. He had come to Lyme from Mevagissey, a fishing village in Cornwall, where he was engineer in charge of a small electricity scheme to light the docks. However, whatever drew him to Lyme, he must have put on a convincing performance on 16th December because at a special council meeting on 29th December the council resolved 'that the streets of the town be lighted by electricity'.

Pulman's Weekly News reported the decision at the start of January. Under the heading, 'Lyme Regis. Proposed Electric Light for the Town', it told readers that at a meeting between the council and the Lyme Regis Electric Light & Power Company Ltd, a scheme for electric light for the town had been provisionally adopted. Mr Alban Woodroffe had written saying that the promoters of the company had invited him to become a director, with power to nominate other directors. He was willing to accept provided the corporation granted the company a contract to light the streets for seven years.

The report continued, 'The company is proposing to light the town using a 100-volt working pressure. For generation, water power will be used as far as possible but the works will be fitted with sufficient machinery to avoid being in any way dependent upon water power.' The total cost of the scheme was put at £1,902. To the ratepayers a further attraction was that the Electric Light Co was offering to provide, at no extra cost, fifteen more lamps than the Gas & Range Co or, if the council preferred, the same number but for £40 less for the year. 'After discussion, the proposition was unanimously carried.'

At 35 Alban Woodroffe was already well-known in the district. His family had moved there in the last years of Victoria's reign and in 1903 he had married Laura Talbot. The Talbots owned Rhode Hill, an estate with a large country house in the neighbouring village of Uplyme. In 1908 Alban inherited the nearby Ware Estate, just across the county border in Devon.

Alban Woodroffe, MBE, JP. 1875 – 1964.

It has been rumoured that he had one of the first motor-cars in Lyme which he drove in a rather Toad-of-Toad-Hall manner, demolishing buildings that got in his way. Also, that under the cover of darkness he conducted experiments with electricity up at Ware House. However, this rather alarming picture hardly matches the facts.

3 THE START

When choosing a chairman, what the promoters of the Electric Light & Power Company would have been looking for was someone well-connected, respectable and able to set a good example to potential shareholders by investing lots of money himself. Alban must have fitted the bill admirably. He knew all the right people, was wealthy and, whatever he had done in his youth (in 1893 when he was 19, his father had sent him off to Argentina to study farm management and bought him an *estancia* – a large cattle ranch – where he spent part of each year through most of his life), in Lyme Regis he was a growing pillar of respectability.

Within a few months of the launch of the company he was a borough councillor, and in 1910 his fellow councillors elected him mayor. In 1914 they chose him again, this time to lead the town throughout the First World War. In 1917 he gave over Rhode Hill, which he had bought from his wife's family, to serve as a hospital for convalescent soldiers. At the end of the war he became High Sheriff of Dorset, a county councillor and chairman of the county education committee. Good going for a man who in 1892 had failed the Army Exam.

Alban went on to be Dorset County Commissioner for Scouts for seven years and chairman of the Lyme Regis Cottage Hospital for twenty-four. He was an Alderman for Dorset and a Justice of the Peace both in Dorset and Devon. In 1932 Lyme Regis awarded him the freedom of the town. The Woodroffe School – the successor to the grammar school he fought for and won for the town – is named after him. And the slurs on his driving skills are almost certainly baseless as, at least later on, he was driven around by his chauffeur.

Back to 1909. On 18th January at 7.30pm there was a closed meeting between the council and Alban Woodroffe and Engineer Balbiani. The press was excluded 'in view of the Special Nature of the business to be dealt with', and the details of the seven-year contract were thrashed out. There would be '90 lamps: 74 of 25 candle-power and 16 of 75 candle-power'. And except when there was bright moonlight, they were to be lit half an hour after local sunset until 11.30pm, or 10.30pm on Sundays. The company would lay 'the wires' underground in the main streets, but overhead elsewhere. The street-lighting contract, worth £240 a year, would commence from June that year.

This was, however, new and unreliable technology. So, 'If a lamp should go out from a broken filament or other cause, the company shall effect repair in 24 hours or pay a penalty'. It would also have to pay the council a rent for the space its lamps took up on their pavements: one penny per lamp per year. Finally, the contract stated that the Electric Light Co would be entitled to dispose of its undertaking to any other company, providing it was not a gas company. Perhaps because of the way the railway companies had taken over the canals and then closed them down, there was a strong mood in the country to prevent the formation of monopolies.

Anyway, with its seven-year contract with the council signed, the Electric Light Co could now set about getting itself properly registered and, more importantly, finding investors to stump up some cash.

On 8th March 1909, the Lyme Regis Electric Light and Power Company Ltd was officially registered with an authorised capital of £5,000. It issued its prospectus four days later, offering 3,500 Ordinary Shares of £1 each. Applications were to be sent with a deposit of 2s.6d* per share to the Wilts & Dorset Banking Co Ltd in Lyme Regis on or before 27th March. The balance of 17s.6d was spread in instalments over the following four months.

---

* See under Money in chapter *25 Postscripts* for notes on the old system of pounds, shillings and pence.

Certificate N° 101894

This Prospectus has been filed with the Registrar of Joint Stock Companies in accordance with the Companies Act, 1900.

The subscription list will close on or before Saturday, the 27th day of March, 1909.

THE LYME REGIS ELECTRIC LIGHT AND POWER COMPANY, LIMITED.

(Incorporated under the Companies Acts, 1862 to 1908.)

AUTHORISED CAPITAL - - £5,000,

DIVIDED INTO

1,000 5 per cent. Preference Shares of £1 each.

4,000 Ordinary Shares of £1 each.

Preferential Shares are preferential as to Capital as well as dividend.

Issue of 3,500 Ordinary Shares of £1 each,

PAYABLE AS FOLLOWS :

2s. 6d. per share on Application, 2s. 6d. per share on Allotment, 5s. 0d. per share two months after allotment, 5s. 0d. per share per month for the two succeeding months.

The minimum subscription upon which the Directors may proceed to Allotment is 50 per cent. of this issue. No Founders' Shares have been or will be issued.

The original prospectus for the Electric Light Company

Of the company's five directors, the occupations of four were described as 'Gentleman'. Of these four, three were local landowners: Wilton Allhusen owned the Pinhay Estate to the west, Douglas Pass had Wootten Fitzpaine Manor near Charmouth, and Alban Woodroffe lived on the Ware Estate. The other two were Alban's brother Philip Woodroffe, 'Gentleman of 96 Piccadilly', and Rowland Browne, an electrical engineer from Birmingham, last heard of in 1919 installing the electricity system in Lorenzo Marques (now Maputo) in Portuguese East Africa (now Mozambique).

The prospectus explained that the company had been formed 'for the purpose of supplying electricity in the charming seaside resort of Lyme Regis and its neighbourhood'. As well as its seven-year contract with the council, the directors expected to secure as customers most of the hotels, the railway station and most of the large shops and private houses in the town.

The company proposed buying 'the Old Malthouse' by the Town Mill off Coombe Street for use as its power station. The price agreed with the owner Edwin Wallis was £200. It also proposed a seven-year agreement with a local builder, William Caddy, in which for £5 a year it would take all the available waterpower from his mill further up the river in order to run a turbine. The company told investors that, to begin with, it aimed to install plant to generate enough electricity to light 1,500 lamps.

The directors estimated the company could make a net profit of £210 per year based on generating costs of 33s 4d per unit and a sales price of 6d per unit. This would provide its investors with a 6 per cent return.

3 THE START

The first shareholders were drawn mainly from the great and good of the district. Among the directors, Douglas Pass invested £1,000, Alban Woodroffe £500 and Wilton Allhusen £100. Rowland Browne and Philip Woodroffe both chipped in £50, the minimum investment for a director. Colonel Robert Williams, the MP for Dorchester, invested £350 and Sir Wilfred Peek, the tea magnate who had built the model Rousden Estate to the west, invested £500. Henry Sturdee, living in Alban's wife's family home at Rhode Hill, and Douglas Pass's mother Elizabeth (described under 'Occupation' as 'Widow') both put up £100. Another widow from Wales and a gentlewoman from Torquay invested small sums, but almost no local residents applied for shares.

Three local men, however, were presented with 20 shares each 'in consideration of their services prior to the formation of the company', and also £60 16s.9d* in cash to share among themselves. These were Thomas Hains, bicycle and motor engineer of Bridge Street; Godfrey Turner, letterpress printer of 42 Broad Street, and John Speed Turner, journalist and publisher of the *Lyme Regis Mirror and Visitors List*, of 5 Broad Street.

Although little else is known about them, the three apparently deserve the credit for bringing electricity to Lyme Regis. In its article at the inauguration, *Pulman's Weekly News* said, 'Mr T. G. Hains must be looked upon as the pioneer of the electric light scheme, as it was mainly through his efforts that Mr C Balbiani, the engineer of the works, was first introduced to the town. Mr Godfrey Turner joined hands with Mr Hains in promoting the scheme.'

Lyme's principal hotel in 1909: *The Alexandra.*

In mid-April the work of installing generating equipment in the Malthouse, wiring up the town and erecting the street lamps began. On 7th May the *Bridport News* reported, 'Aided by glorious weather, the contractors have been able for the past three weeks to make very considerable progress in the fixing of poles and laying of cables.'

There were, however, complaints about the unsightliness of the poles, and the council responded by forming a sub-committee to control as far as possible their sites. In any case, the Bridport News pragmatically observed, 'Had an underground cable been demanded for the whole borough, there would have been no electric light.'

* See 'Money' in chapter *25 Postscripts* for notes on the pre-decimal currency-system of pounds, shillings and pence.

A gang of labourers laying the first cables in Bridge Street in May 1909.

On 25th May *Pulman's Weekly* reported, 'the undertaking to light the town with electricity is being rapidly pushed forward and is well nigh complete. This week two of the workmen were injured. While pouring out some hot pitch from a bucket, Mr D. Board from Ottery St Mary severely burnt his right hand, and a man named White suffered a broken leg from a paving slab falling on it.' Both men were conveyed to the cottage hospital, where Mr White's injured limb was set by Dr Harry Cooper, Admiralty Surgeon and Borough Councillor, who lived above the Cobb in a fine Regency house called Belmont.

The injuries may well have resulted from the rush to finish the job on time. The contractors, Johnson & Phillips from Charlton in Kent, were trying to complete the entire project in just seven weeks so that the lights could go on on 1st June. How Mr White managed to have a paving slab fall on his leg is unexplained, but Mr Board's burnt hand probably resulted from the use of pitch as an electrical insulator. Where they were laid underground, the practice was to suspend bare wires on insulators in a shallow wooden and metal trough, and then fill it with pitch. Anyway, despite the complaints and accidents, on the evening of 1st June 1909 the lights went on.

The cottage hospital building from 1897 to 1928, opposite the parish church and with the National School beyond.

THE LIGHTS GO ON

The inaugural ceremony was covered in detail by the local press. In an article headed, 'Inauguration Of The Electric Light. Important And Interesting Event', the *Bridport News* painted the picture. At the Malthouse 'a whole army of workmen have been employed altering and redecorating the premises to suit the requirements necessary for the production of light'. Engineer Balbiani had been 'engaged most assiduously in supervising the preparations for, and the erection of, the various machinery. The motive power at the station is supplied by an oil engine, while at the Higher Mill, near Horn Bridge, the Company are putting in a turbine to utilise the water for generating purposes.'

Pulman's Weekly told readers that, with a working fall of 18 feet of water at Higher Mill, nine horse-power per minute should be obtained. 'Some twelve miles of wire have been extended along the streets, while aluminium wire has been very extensively used for aerial work. It is understood that this is the first time that aluminium wire has been used in England for such a purpose, and consequently the experiment will be watched with much interest by the engineering world.'

The ceremony was splendid. 'Although, owing to the wet weather the streets were in a very dirty condition, this did not seem to damp the enthusiasm of the townspeople, who came forth in great numbers to witness the new illumination.' By eight o'clock the streets were blocked by 'upwards of 1,000 persons, the majority being around the Power Station, where the police, under Sgt. Bishop kept complete order.'

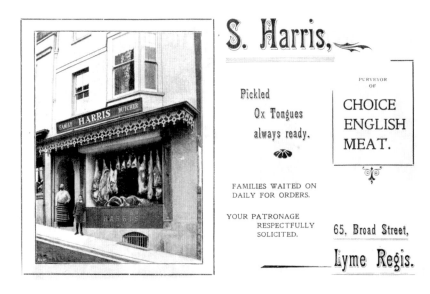

An advertisement for Sam Harris's shop in the town guide. The large figure is almost certainly Mayor Harris himself

16

4 THE LIGHTS GO ON

Punctually at nine o'clock, a procession wended its way from the Guildhall to the Malthouse. His Worship the Mayor Alderman Sam Harris wore his scarlet robes and chain of office, and was attended by his two mace-bearers. Behind them came former mayor Councillor J.O'Neil, Alderman Bickley, Alderman Rendall and eleven councillors. They were followed by the various borough officers: the town clerk, the medical officer of health, the water bailiff, the harbour master, the clerk to the burial board, the borough surveyor, the assistant overseer, and the borough treasurer and auditors. Engineer Balbiani and prominent local tradesmen brought up the rear.

'They proceeded to the power station where the Mayor was welcomed by Mr Alban J.Woodroffe, chairman of the directors of the Company. The entrance to the Power Station had been specially covered in for the occasion, and was brilliantly illuminated by electricity and bedecked with flags, kindly lent by Mr W.C. Darby. A halt was made in the engine room where, with the aid of a gold-covered switch, the Mayor formally inaugurated the lighting scheme, and the townspeople cheered lustily as the new illuminant made its appearance in the streets of the town.'

1909   The 'unsightly poles' on the Marine Parade complained of at the inauguration.

In a brief speech Mayor Harris thanked Alban Woodroffe for the service the company was rendering the townspeople in introducing electric light. In Alban's reply, however, there was a hint of bitterness. The poles carrying the cable along the Marine Parade had been criticised as 'unsightly'. Perhaps that was true, but he had to point out that the company had already laid more cable underground than their contract required. If more townspeople had invested in the scheme by becoming shareholders, the poles on 'the Esplanade' would not have been necessary. Even now the company was prepared 'to put that section of the work underground if the townspeople would take up in shares the estimated outlay of £300, and the cable could be buried in time for the summer season. (Applause)'.

Alban Woodroffe then invited the gathering 'to join him in partaking in a glass of wine. The procession was thereupon re-formed and proceeded to the Guildhall where champagne and biscuits were handed round.'

At the Guildhall, reports describe how toasts were proposed, drunk and responded to. Mayor Sam Harris suggested that, 'the people will get used to the poles in time', but a voice in the crowd shouted, 'Never!'. Ex-Mayor O'Neil opined that instead of quibbling about the poles, the townspeople should subscribe the necessary money to have them buried. ('Hear, hear.') Sam Harris, who owned the biggest butcher's shop in Broad Street, added that he had intended taking a few shares, although he was a poor man (laughter), but he did not do so as he did not wish to take sides (applause). The singing of the National Anthem terminated the proceedings.

Back in January the cost of the scheme had been estimated at £1,902. A week after the lights went on, George Henley, the local chemist who had been appointed the Electric Light Co's auditor, provided shareholders with an updated estimate of the preliminary expenses.

Promotion	£300 0s.0d
Building	£450 0s.0d
Offices and establishment	£40 0s.0d
Plant	£765 0s.0d
Construction, mains and public lighting	£1,400 0s.0d
Contracting Dept.	£130 0s.0d
	£3,085 0s.0d

One of the new street lamps in Broad Street in about 1910. Note the stump of old gas lamp beside it, which Wallis-the-gas would not remove. The bay window and early AA-sign further up the street belong to The Three Cups Hotel where, in 1948, this story ends.

4 THE LIGHTS GO ON

The small number of local investors must have disappointed Alban Woodroffe. By the inauguration a total of 18 investors had been allotted 3,003 shares in the company. But of those 18, only three were Lyme Regis residents – a draper, an ironmonger and a schoolmaster – and between them they had just 55 shares.

Interestingly, none of the major shareholders in the company lived close enough to be able to benefit directly from the mains by connecting their own homes to it. Cynics may think the motivation of those first shareholders was purely financial: they just wanted to make a profit. However, I suspect in that age they were also driven by a good dose of patriotism. Electricity was the new technology, and Britain and the Empire needed it. The project therefore demanded their support.

Despite the excitement at the June inauguration, the scheme failed to attract much more local investment. In July a painter and decorator, a hairdresser and someone describing herself as a 'Gentlewoman' invested £5 each, and William Caddy, the builder who had leased the waterpower from Higher Mill to the company, put in £25. In August, a Colonel Fowler bought 200 shares. In January 1910 Cecil Street of Summerhill* bought 207 shares and Alban Woodroffe a further 100 shares. Only in June 1910 were the last of the 3,500 originally authorised shares taken up, yielding £3,452 10s.0d cash. (The difference between this sum and the £3,500 face value of the share capital is explained by the cash and free shares presented to Thomas Hains and the Turner brothers by the board as a reward for dreaming the whole scheme up.) Nevertheless, although local support for the scheme had been less than overwhelming, by the end of 1909 the lights in Lyme were well and truly on.

* This house became the world-famous Summerhill 'freedom school' created by educationalist A.S.Neill from 1923 to 1927, when he moved it to Norfolk after a fire.

UP AND RUNNING

S o it was that on 1st June 1909, Lyme Regis became the first town in Dorset with a public electricity supply: a part engine-powered, part water-powered 110-volt DC system. How many consumers there were at the start is not recorded, but by the end of the Electric Light & Power Company's first full financial year, in March 1911, there were fifty-seven. These will have included the homes of some of the wealthier private residents, the better hotels and pubs, the main shops and offices, and anyone else who wanted to show they were thoroughly go-ahead. For the time being, however, the Electric Light Co's financial mainstay was its seven-year contract with the borough council for the town's 90 street lamps: '16 of 75 candle power and 74 of 25 candle power, to be lit at a cost of £240 per annum.'

In those days 'candle power' was the unit used to express the brightness of a lamp. According to information from the archivist at the Institution of Electrical Engineers, one candle power is defined as the light emitted by a spermaceti candle weighing 1/6 lb (91 grams) burning at a rate of 120 grains (7.8 grams) per hour. According to the first edition of the *Shorter Oxford English Dictionary*, spermaceti is a fatty substance found in the head of the sperm-whale and other whales and dolphins, used largely in medicinal preparations, and in the manufacture of candles. And according to which website you consult, one candle power is either 10.76 lumens or 12.57 lumens, the units used today to express the brightness of lamps.

The box of my Osram Classic Pearl 100 watt light bulb says it gives out a brightness of 1,360 lumens so, depending on which equivalence you chose, its brightness is either 108 or 126 candle power. It hardly matters. The point is that by modern standards those street lamps in Lyme Regis in 1909 were astonishingly dim. The 16 main lamps of 75 candle power gave out only as much light as a modern 60 or 70 watt bulb, and the remaining 74 lamps a very weedy 20 watts each. The town's entire street lighting system used around 2½kWs in total – about the same power as a single modern electric kettle. And of course, as with the gas lamps they replaced, the electric street lights were only lit for a few hours each night and, when the moon and stars were bright, not even then.

For private homes, the company's prospectus had proposed a target of '1,500 lamps of 8 c.p each'. Quite what use a lamp of such impressive dimness would be is hard for us to imagine, but the early carbon filament bulbs gave out no less light than many gas lamps of the time, and were of course cleaner, easier to control and safer.

Across the river from the Malthouse generating station stood the ancient Town Mill. From the Middle Ages the Malthouse and Mill had been part of the same business, the one providing large amounts of malted grain for the other to grind for making beer. Sensible people did not drink water. For centuries the Mill and Malthouse belonged to the borough. However, at the start of Queen Victoria's reign the council effectively privatised them, selling them off to a miller called William Wallis for the sum of £305.

Through most of the Victorian Age the Town Mill prospered under Wallis and his son, but by the end of the century it was in difficulties and was leased to a succession of tenant millers. Then in 1909 William's grandson Edwin Wallis sold off the Malthouse from the Mill for £200

£200 to the Electric Light Co to be its generating station. Intriguingly, the owner of the Lyme Regis Gas and Range Co at that time was a Mr W.R. Wallis and, very probably, Edwin and he were first cousins. If that were so, it is not unreasonable to suppose that Edwin's sale of the Malthouse to the Electric Light Co may have resulted in a chill in relations between the two cousins.

Be that as it may, the Wallis family remained an important but declining feature on the town's landscape for the next decade or so. The borough water-rate book of 1913 shows Lyme's biggest property-owner in terms of numbers of houses was Mr W.R. Wallis with about eighty. Next came Edwin Wallis with fifteen. Only in third place was the Lord of the Manor, Colonel Henry Henley, from the long-established Henley family who were the principal landowners in the borough and now lived away on their estate at Winsham near Chard. The colonel owned a mere dozen houses in town. By the 1920s, however, Mrs Edwin Wallis was advertising rooms to let in Holmcroft, their large house on Broad Street, and W.R.'s Gas & Range Co had been sold to a firm in Exeter. In the 1930s Edwin Wallis had two of his cottages near old Jordan Mill compulsorily demolished under a slum clearance order.

The Town Mill c. 1890.

For its first few months of operation, the Electric Light Co provided the town's electricity from a single generating set (a Gardner horizontal paraffin engine, probably second-hand, turning a Morris Hawkins dynamo) in the Malthouse. The water turbine promised in the prospectus had yet to come on stream. The obvious place to have sited this would have been across the river in the Town Mill but the Mill was still using its waterpower to grind corn.
It was therefore at Higher Mill, half a mile upstream, that sometime later in 1909 the water turbine started work. It was a 'Trent' model by Gilkes & Co of Cumbria, 'specially designed for driving a dynamo direct', and 'it cost the company £63 9s.9d.

In early October 1909 the council made its first payment to the Electric Light Co for public lighting: £36 10s.0d for the two months of June and July. This is slightly less than one would expect from the contract rate of £20 per month, suggesting that, at the time of the June inauguration, some of the street lights had still to be connected. The payment for the following quarter was for the full £60.

A Gilkes 'Trent' turbine of the type installed at Higher Mill

In the same month the council passed a vote of thanks to Alban Woodroffe for a gift of shrubs for George's Square off Coombe Street, the space his father had bequeathed the town for public use. And it received a request from the Electric Light Co for the return of a £40 'road breaking deposit'. Evidently when it agreed to let the company dig up its roads to lay cables, the council wanted a guarantee they would be put back tidily. Eventually only £33 3s.0d was returned, suggesting the restoration work was less than satisfactory.

There was also the problem of Mr Wallis's 75 defunct gas lamps, standing forlorn around the town. The council asked him to take them away but he was in no hurry. After two years their patience ran out: they declared the lamps 'constituted a nuisance' and had them removed.

The Malthouse (left) and the Town Mill with the river between in 1982. Note the brick battery-house at the far end of the Malthouse, the electricity van, and the 'temporary' corrugated iron roof put on after the fire in 1947.

At the council elections on 1st November Alban Woodroffe offered himself 'to the burgesses of the borough' – those entitled to vote, which by that time meant all men aged over 21 – and was elected. He remained chairman of the Electric Light Co. The unsightly poles and overhead cables along the Marine Parade were still an issue, and in the spring he wrote to the town clerk offering a solution. The company would place the cables underground along the length of the Parade if in return the council extended its street-lighting contract with the company from seven years to ten. Back at the start of 1909, several councillors had queried whether there was really a need for a contract as long as seven years. Now the extension to ten years was passed without question. After all, they had got to know Alban Woodroffe.

At about the same time, Engineer Balbiani showed he also had business skills. For an extra charge of £9 a year, he offered to extend the mains westwards in the town to the Woodmead Road, and erect three street lamps there. But, he added, if just one private consumer in the road could be persuaded to connect, he would cut the council's bill to £8.

On 22nd February 1910, *Pulman's Weekly* reported, 'A gale on Monday night was responsible for breaking overhead cables shortly after seven o'clock in the evening with the resulting failure of the electric light. The damage was repaired expeditiously by the Company's engineer, Mr Balbiani, so that the streets were only in darkness for about 15 minutes, although almost an hour had elapsed after the mishap before the occupiers of private houses and business establishments could avail themselves of the electric light.' We can picture Engineer Balbiani up some ladder with a hurricane-lamp, struggling to repair his precious cables in the teeth of the gale. Health and safety regulations in those days were probably still confined to blast-furnaces, cotton mills and children working down the mines.

5 UP AND RUNNING

When in May 1910 King Edward VII died, the council sent a telegram of condolence to the Royal Family and the vicar gave every child at the national school a black ribbon to wear in a mourning bow. They also got a half-holiday to mark George V being proclaimed King.

May 1910. The Proclamation of George V's ascent to the throne being read to the crowd in Church Street. Note the women below, the men above and the fire brigade with their brass helmets paraded on the left.

Slowly the Electric Light Co was adding customers, and the first payment to the company by the borough council itself for anything other than street lighting appeared that May.

In 1892 Captain Nicholas Marder had died leaving £4,500 in his will to build six almshouses in Coombe Street 'for the repose of ancient sea-farers of good character'. We can guess that he had served a lifetime at sea and had no children of his own because in May 1910 his nephew, a Major Marder, made a gift through the Council to the occupants of the almshouses. It comprised 'six pipes, a quantity of tobacco, some seeds for flowers and vegetables, and six pictures', possibly of kind old Captain Marder, or of mermaids, or of the good major himself.

Anyway, May was the month when the first of a series of payments to the Electric Light Co of 13s.4d per quarter for the Marder Bequest Almshouses first appears in the records. For some reason the council must have decided that the ancient seafarers were worth electrifying.

However, despite new business, a year after the lights first went on there is a suggestion in council records that things were not going as well for the Electric Light Co as expected. On 10th June a special council meeting was held 'to consider the expediency of acquiring the electricity undertaking from the Lyme Regis Electric Light & Power Company Limited. Mr A.J.Woodroffe fully explained the present financial and general position of the company.' The matter was adjourned and, when it met a month later, the council bluntly resolved 'not to entertain the offer'.

So in August Alban Woodroffe invested another £200 in the company himself and a further £100 in October, raising his total investment to 900 shares. At the same time Cecil Street of Summerhill and Edward Ffooks (one of the five original telephone subscribers) of the Sundial put in £100 each. But despite this extra cash, in November 1910 the company lodged a £500 debenture bond with Lloyds Bank 'against the electricity undertaking and all its property': it had had to borrow £500 from the bank.

The Town Hall, alias the Guildhall

In the same month his fellow councillors elected Alban Woodroffe Mayor of Lyme Regis for the first time, and the 1911 edition of *Kelly's Directory* named Cecil Street as the manager of the Electric Light Co. At some time in 1910 Engineer Balbiani must have moved on to pastures new.

As well as the Town Hall or Guildhall – it never could make up its mind – the council owned a number of other buildings in Lyme Regis including the Assembly Rooms (where Jane Austen had danced) and their extension, the Victoria Hall. These were let out for various functions and, in January 1911, to the boy scouts* for £7 a year to include lighting. That February, the council agreed to a recommendation by Alderman Bickley that 'incandescent burners' (brighter gas lamps) be placed in the Town Hall and Committee Room, and gave Bickley's committee power to install them in the Assembly Rooms too if they thought fit.

They did not. Instead they chose to illuminate the Assembly Rooms (and boy scouts) with electricity. Mr W R Wallis of the Gas & Range Co was not at all happy and wrote to the mayor to complain. Why, he demanded, had the new lighting not been put out to tender? Alderman Bickley replied, 'The Committee considered that electric light was the best light for public rooms, and received an offer to amply light the whole building from the Electric Light & Power Company for £5 0s.0d. The Committee therefore accepted the offer.'

Nevertheless, the council's accounts for May show that gas, coke and coal remained by far the most important source of heat and light for its own buildings (and the rest of the town's):

Electric Light & Power Co. Ltd	*Wiring Assembly Rooms for Electric Light*	*£5 0s.0d*
" " "	*Current – Assembly Rooms*	*5s.2d*
" " "	*Marder Bequest*	*13s.4d*
Bradford and Sons	*Coals etc*	*£1 2s.11d*
Gas & Range Company	*Gas, Town Hall and Assembly Rooms*	*£2 10s.0d*
" " "	*Coke*	*2s.4d*

*Robert Baden-Powell, founder of the Boy Scout movement, had held their first summer camp in Dorset in 1907 and published *Scouting for Boys* the following year. He and Alban Woodroffe were personal friends.

In spring 1911 the Electric Light Co published its first set of accounts for the year to 31st March. Income from the council for 'public lighting' accounted for about half its total revenue of £526 17s.0d. There were 57 private and business consumers with a total of 947 lamps between them. If you exclude the 90 street lamps, this means that each premises had on average only about 15 lamps. Count the lamps in your own home and you will see how few by modern standards that is, especially given that these were the larger houses in town.

The report went on to say the amount of electricity taken by private consumers had doubled over the year. The company's costs had been £158 on salaries and wages and £71 on fuel and

Higher Mill, site of the first water turbine.

oil. The water turbine at Higher Mill had supplied 21 per cent of the total current generated. It concluded with the news that the cottage and office it was building for its engineer, on a plot at 5a Coombe Street which backed on to the Malthouse, was almost complete.

The population of Lyme Regis according to the 1911 census published in April was 2,772 'including 473 on board one of His Majesty's ships'. In May the Electric Light Co asked the council to rent it a small piece of land in front of its new 'Electricity Cottage' in Coombe Street 'to place a few flowering plants therein and so improve the appearance of that part of the street'. And to keep the boy scouts in the Assembly Rooms under control, the council let out the Victoria Hall for cookery classes for girls. The rent included solid fuel for the stove. In those days no-one in the town would have dreamed of using electricity for cooking.

King George V   1910-1936.

To celebrate the coronation on 12th June of George V (full title, 'King of Great Britain, Ireland, the British Dominions Beyond the Seas and Emperor of India'), the council gave the Coronation Committee free use of the Assembly Rooms, and sanctioned with thanks the

Electric Light Co's offer to illuminate them on coronation night for free. At its next meeting on 10th July the council passed a vote of thanks to the company for their 'excellent illumination' of the building and granted a Miss Wilkinson permission to give musical entertainments on the sea front, subject to her conforming with Police Regulations.

The Electric Light Co was working hard to sell the benefits of electric lighting, but if the free coronation night illuminations had been an attempt to tempt the council to connect up the Guildhall, it failed. An offer to completely wire the building for just £5 was declined. The council said it 'could not justify the expense of the Electric Light considering the sum now paid for gas is only about £2 per quarter'. Many rate-payers would continue to regard electricity as a luxury for years to come, and councillors were anxious to avoid any charge of extravagance. It was not for another twenty years, in 1932, that councillors finally instructed the borough electrical engineer to prepare plans to light the town hall with electricity.

In July 1911 the Post Office published a new telephone directory of southern England. The number of subscribers in Lyme Regis had increased since 1909 from seven to eighteen. Now you could ring the police, the railway station, a butcher, a blacksmith, a plumber and six private subscribers, but still not a doctor.

Apart from a handful of almshouses, there was no social housing in the town. Most working class families lived in rented accommodation owned by private landlords like the Wallises. Many of these cottages were old, dark, damp and cramped, and the School Attendance Committee complained that 'certain children have to be frequently dismissed from school on account of their dirty condition'. The council brought the problem to the attention of Dr Spurr, the borough medical officer of health. In his report he described the children as 'verminous'.

So in 1911 the council agreed to build its first council houses – what it then described as 'workmen's dwellings'. There were to be twelve, in three blocks of four on a field by the gas works, which it bought from Colonel Henley, Lord of the Manor, for £730. The building contract, worth £2,143 6s.0d for the houses plus £35 for the road and £81 for the sewers, went to an Axminster firm. Inspired with civic pride, the council named its new development Corporation Terrace and a year later decided to add eight more, bringing the total to twenty. When Dr Spurr inspected them he reported they were all in good order.

The road surfaces in the town at that time consisted of crushed granite, flint and limestone. Horses and other animals also contributed. To keep the streets level and maintained, they were regularly rolled by a great 10-ton steamroller and watered by horse-drawn water carts to wash away dirt and in summer keep the dust down.

Until now the water carts had been filled from mains hydrants around the town. However, the low or non-existent water pressure in the mains was a regular source of complaint, especially in the summer and from consumers who lived up the hills. The council therefore decided to try to fill the carts directly from the river, and asked Mr Street of the Electric Light Co for advice. He recommended a pump from the Pulsometer Engineering Company, which he was prepared to supply and install down by the Malthouse for £24 15s.0d. It would fill a water-cart in 4½ minutes for ⅓d and horses could then haul water around the lower parts of the town without the need to drain the mains.

In August 1911 the bill from the Electric Light Co for the quarter was £62 for public lighting plus 2s.6d for the electric pump. In September 1911 Alban Woodroffe bought another 300 shares in the Electric Light Co and a Mr Thomas Budgett from Lyme bought 200 shares.

These were the last investments made in the original company and we can only speculate about Alban's motive. He might have wanted to encourage and reassure Mr Budgett, who shortly afterwards became a director. He might have still been genuinely optimistic about the company's prospects. Or he might have developed a sense of personal responsibility for the company, and seen it as his duty to keep it afloat. In any case these further 300 shares brought Alban's total investment to £1,200; this at a time when the national average wage for an unskilled male worker was £54 a year. (Women employees, almost invariably unmarried as when they got married they were expected to retire to look after the home, could expect less than half the wage for a man: about £28 a year.)

At the start of 1912 the council took what today seems the extraordinary decision: 'That during those months in the year when bathing is not in season, any rubbish that is not injurious to public health may be deposited in the sea at Cobb Gate.' There was also a lot of surplus clay to be got rid of from a new section of the cemetery, and as Borough Surveyor Frederick McDonnell was unsure what to do with it, the council told him to throw it in the sea too.

In May the council agreed to let the Assembly Rooms free to Mrs Radford for 'an entertainment in aid of the Titanic Relief Fund': the liner had sunk that April with the loss of 1,500 lives and the public was appalled. Shortly afterwards they gave a Mr Ellis part of the building on a three-year lease, with permission to put up a sign on the balcony saying 'Cinema'. Two years later, he sold it on to John Raymond, who ran the Assembly Rooms cinema with his wife until the end of the 1920s when the council demolished the buildings to make way for a more profitable car park.

In June 1912 the directors of the Lyme Regis Electric Light & Power Co gave the council notice that they intended to sell it to the County of Dorset Electric Supply Co Ltd. This was a new much larger company. Its name described its ambition, and its flotation in September raised £20,935. The original investors included the Bournemouth and Poole Electric Light Co with 2,068 shares, Callanders Cable & Construction Co with 2,000 shares and Crompton & Co* with 2,000 shares. After a couple of Devon engineers and a London solicitor, Alban Woodroffe was the fourth largest private investor, with 773 shares.

The following summer all the local Electric Light Co directors except Alban resigned and were replaced by new directors: Dr Hosker from Boscombe, Lt Col Castleman-Smith from Blandford, Captain Williams from Wimborne and Walter Baxter, a brewer from Sherborne. These and Alban were also directors of the new holding company, the County of Dorset Supply Co. How much the original Lyme Regis company investors got for their shares is not recorded, but only Alban Woodroffe and Douglas Pass bothered to invest in the new company. Quite possibly for the others it was a case of once bitten, twice shy.

In October 1912 a local solicitor, Harold Ramsbotham, was appointed town clerk, a key position he was to hold in the changing town for more than twenty years. And in November Alderman Henry Octavius ('Henry the Eighth') Bickley JP, draper, milliner, costumier and outfitter of Broad Street, followed Alban Woodroffe as mayor, a post he had last held in 1900 when Victoria was on the throne.

---

*Colonel R E B Crompton (1845 – 1940) was a leading pioneer of Britain's electrical industry. His company manufactured generators and provided the first electricity supply to Kensington. He championed the advantages of DC (direct current) systems. The original generating equipment at Higher Mill, and also possibly at the Malthouse, included Crompton dynamos.

H. O. Bickley,

ARTISTIC MILLINERY,
MANTLES, COATS, etc.
HIGH-CLASS DRESSMAKING

Visiting and Evening Gowns.
Blouses. Gloves. Corsets.

FURNISHING DRAPERY.
CARPETS. LINOLEUMS.

Gentlemen's Complete Outfitting.

26 & 27, Broad Street,

Lyme Regis.

Mayor Bickley's shop.

The borough water-rate book for 1913 shows that 5a Coombe Street, the electrical engineer's house and office, was owned by the Electric Light Co, had a rateable value of £10 and was occupied by Frederick Cheshire. Mr Cheshire had clearly taken over from Cecil Street of Summerhill as the company's manager-engineer, quite possibly at the time the Dorset Electric Supply Co took over the company. Cecil Street had probably cashed in his shares and returned to a gentlemanly existence up the hill.

In June 1913, Mayor Bickley opened the town's new park, the Langmoor Gardens, on land above the Marine Parade. The town had bought the land from Alban Woodroffe's mother-in-law Mrs Talbot with the aid of a large bequest. Alban and Dr Cooper presented shrubs and rock plants.

In October the first mention appeared in council records of what was to become an escalating problem: 'the lamp out'. This was defined as one street lamp not working for one night, and 133 lamps out were recorded in the quarter to 30th September. When the electric lights first arrived, people had regarded them with a proper degree of admiration and respect. Now they just wanted them to work. The company agreed to knock off 2d for each 'lamp out' from its billto the Council.

It was also reported that Edwin Wallis, who had sold the Mill in 1912 but still owned two cottages opposite the Malthouse in Mill Lane, had failed to install a flush toilet in one of them despite being ordered to do so at the start of the year. The council sent Town Clerk Ramsbotham round to warn him that unless he did, the council would take steps. Back in 1910 Mr Wallis had put in a formal complaint about the smell from the sewers in Coombe Street so he was not in a strong position to resist sanitary improvements.

Coombe Street in about 1907. The angle of the photo and the size of the people give the impression of a much larger street than in fact it is. 'Electricity Cottage' will be built at 5a Coombe Street in 1911, behind the three men standing on the right.

The final accounts for the independent Electric Light Co for the year to April 1913 show its income had risen to £820 0s.5d. For the next nine months to December 31st 1913, when the Dorset Electric Supply Co's new accountancy period took over, it made a profit of £155 5s.5d The Dorset Supply Co's profit was £653 14s 6d. According to *Garckes Manual** for 1913, the number of consumers in town had risen from 57 to 70, and the number of light bulbs from 947 to 1,147. So things electrical in Lyme Regis looked reasonably rosy.

Not so at the cement works, which was far more important to most people in the town. Medical Officer of Health Dr Spurr noted that, along with building and fishing, the works provided the principal occupation in the town. Along with its associated brick works, in its heyday it had employed up to 375 people. However, now there were growing complaints about its smoke pollution.

The Lyme Regis Cement Company dated back to 1850. Its factory, built on the Monmouth Beach beyond the Cobb, was owned by the lords of the manor, the Henley family, and was right in the path of the prevailing wind. It made a famous quick-setting 'hydraulic cement', particularly useful for harbour works, which was shipped around the Empire directly from the Cobb.

The raw materials for the cement were the fossil-rich blue lias and 'cementstones' which make up the restless grey cliffs. To start with the company had collected fallen blocks off the beach but now it was blasting the cliffs and also quarrying stone from the sea bed at low tide.

After hauling in the rocks, the process of making the cement involved roasting them in two coal-fired kilns. Although these had tall chimneys, by 1912 smoke from the fires and 'polluting sulphurous fumes' and dust from the rock was a serious problem for residents

Garckes Manual of Electrical Undertakings was an annual directory giving details of all municipal and private electricity companies.

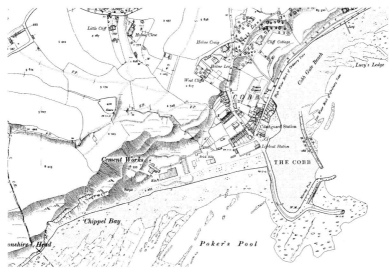

The cement works on the Monmouth Beach south west of the town.

around the Cobb, and summer visitors to the beach. A steam locomotive used for hauling materials around the beach added to the nuisance.

That July, 36 residents signed a petition asking for action. In October, the company's chairman had a meeting with the council and promised 'to abate the smoke nuisance'. That action was to raise the chimneys higher; however, rather than solving the problem it just

The cement works on the Monmouth Beach.

spread it further afield. The following June Mrs Clarke, who lived up above the town, wrote to the council complaining of the damage done to her kitchen garden and apple trees by a deposit of white dust from the works and the smoke. 'The heightening of the chimneys is the cause', she said. In the five years she had lived there it had never happened before.

Remains of the cement works railway tracks on the Monmouth Beach today.

By 1914 the council was taking legal advice and even proposed holding a post-card poll of the burgesses (voters) to gauge support for forcing the works to close. Meanwhile it banned the company's lorry from driving onto the Cobb quay because of the structural damage that might cause. Then just before war broke out, the company's cement boat was requisitioned. The council gave temporary permission for it to use the steep Cobb Road to get coal in and its cement out but, whether because of these local restrictions or the war, in August 1915 the company terminated its tenancy of some stores it rented on the Cobb and went into receivership. For the next 20 years the works lay derelict.

In February 1914 at the end of a council meeting, Alban Woodroffe led a little troop of his fellow-councillors to the Cobb to inspect the place where he wanted permission to moor his yacht. In March permission was given: 'Mr A J Woodroffe is to be allowed to occupy for the next two years a space inside the north wall 100 ft long and 20 ft wide, and to erect two posts at each end to be joined together by boards, any expense to be borne by Mr Woodroffe, including the shifting of a flight of steps.'

Alban Woodroffe's yacht 'Sheila', which he kept moored on the Cobb.

For the quarter to the end of February 1914, the council paid the Electric Light Co £62 18s.2d for lighting the streets plus eight shillings more for filling up the street-watering carts with its new electric pump. In May it appointed a consultant engineer to report on the borough's failing water supply.

That spring the local newspapers carried worrying stories about trouble brewing across the sea. Oddly though, the stories seemed far more concerned with Ireland than with Germany.

WAR

In years to come, people would look back on the summer of 1914 as marking the end of a golden age. The hallmarks of Edwardian England were stable prices and wages, steady technical progress and a rigid social structure which, even if they didn't like it, people understood. Over the next four years, the war to end all wars touched everyone in the country and life grew increasingly bleak.

At the start, however, Victorian habits of thought rather than soldiers were still firmly entrenched. On 4th August, while Germany was busy invading Belgium, Mayor Bickley presided over the petty sessions in the Guildhall as the borough's chief magistrate. In those days, doling out justice was part of the mayor's job.

Mayor Henry Octavius Bickley.

Before him stood an errand boy aged 14 who had stolen a purse (containing £1 13s. 10½d) while delivering to the cottage of Miss Sophia Frost. The lad had admitted the offence to Constable Meech and appeared in court with his father. *Pulman's Weekly* continued, 'The Mayor told the boy he must think himself lucky he was not going to be sent to a reformatory school'. His sentence was to order the father 'to chastise the boy in the presence of a policeman', and also to bind the father over for 12 months on a surety of £10 for his son's good behaviour. Presumably the requirement for a policeman to be present at the chastisement was to make sure the father beat his son neither too gently nor too hard. For a working man in those days, £10 was equivalent to nearly three months' wages.

On 14th September, under a heading in council minutes 'Public Lighting and the War', Councillor Woodroffe told his fellow councillors that, as they had probably noticed in the press, now the country was at war the Admiralty was advising local authorities in coastal towns to reduce bright lights along the sea front. He has therefore been to see Mr Raymond at the Assembly Rooms cinema. Mr Raymond had kindly agreed to extinguish the lights on the side of the building facing the sea.

A week later, councillors were informed that a 24-hour watch had been set on the town's waterworks because of the danger that 'aliens' might try to poison their water supply. According to the chief constable, the military authorities had reported three separate cases of attempted poisonings of waterworks. They went on to discuss erecting and fitting out a little hut at the waterworks for a permanent watchmen. At the following meeting, however, they agreed that on reflection it was 'most improbable that any serious-minded alien would trouble about a supply as we have here'. They discontinued the watch and thanked the boy scouts for the loan of their tents.

In the early autumn a number of refugees from Belgium arrived in the town and the local newspapers carried patriotic reports of British victories and German defeats, or at least of what one report described as German 'unsportsmanlike' behaviour. 'Appalling savagery', 'Eight Days of Pillage and Massacre' etc. At home, local auctioneer Mr Radford complained that his neighbour, Dr Cooper of the Cottage Hospital, had taken to keeping pigs in the garden of Belmont, his house overlooking the Cobb. The council instructed Medical Officer of Health Dr Spurr to investigate the matter. He reported back that he could find no nuisance so the council sided with the pigs. In the past the medical officer of health had criticised in his annual reports the hygienic condition of some of Mr Radford's rental properties, so the council may have felt Mr Radford was in no position to start throwing stones.

Belmont – the home of Dr Cooper and his pigs.

At the beginning of November the aldermen and councillors unanimously elected Alban Woodroffe Mayor of Lyme Regis for the 12 twelve months, and continued to elect him year by year throughout the war. In the same month Chief Officer Captain Foxwell reported that five members of the town's Victoria Fire Brigade had joined the colours, and been replaced with a Mr Chick and eight boy scouts.

On 20th November the *Bridport News* carried a piece headed 'Mayor's Sunday'. 'Sunday being the first Sunday after the choosing of a new Mayor, Councillor A.J.Woodroffe, who has been elected to the office of Chief Magistrate of the borough, attended Divine service at the Roman Catholic Church in state'.

The report described how, 'despite a wet and somewhat boisterous morning', the civic dignitaries had assembled at the Guildhall to hear the town band play the various allies' national anthems: Britain, France, Belgium, Italy, Russia and, presumably if they could find the music, Japan. The band then led a procession up the long steep hill to the Catholic church. Next came, in order, the boy scouts, the fire brigade, the mayor's macebearers, the borough police under Sergeant Stockley and then Mayor Woodroffe himself, resplendent in robes and chain. Aldermen Rendall, Bickley and Harris and a dozen councillors puffed along behind. Town Clerk Ramsbotham, Surveyor McDonnell and all the other borough officials brought up the rear.

'The church was filled to its utmost capacity, the congregation including the Belgian refugees being cared for by the borough.' The Bishop of Plymouth delivered the sermon and impressed the *Bridport News* reporter by then addressing the Belgian refugees 'in their native tongue'. A Father Smith from Exeter 'ably presided at the organ'. The size of this attendance at a Catholic service, given Lyme's long non-conformist tradition, and at the top of that hill, is an indication of Alban Woodroffe's personal popularity.

By the end of 1914, 'to reduce the exhibition of lights skywards and seawards in accordance with guidelines from the naval and military authoritories', the council had turned off all the lamps along the Marine Parade. Alderman Bickley was given power to take any further action he and the chief constable felt necessary to make the town invisible from the sea at night. The Home Office wrote later to say the precautions taken in Lyme Regis were 'most satisfactory'.

In the year to 31st December 1914, the Electric Light Co made a profit of £501 19s.0d on sales of £1,076 18s.9d, which included about £50 from renting electricity meters to its customers. In those days you paid separately for your current and for the equipment the company obliged you to hire to tell you how much you owed. The Lyme Regis company paid its shareholders, the County of Dorset Electric Supply Co, a dividend of 10 per cent and the latter's profits reached an all-time peak of £813 8s.4d.

At the start of 1915, the grim reality of war arrived in Lyme. In bright moonlight* at 2am on January 1st, a German submarine torpedoed *HMS Formidable* 35 miles out in Lyme Bay. 'One of the worst south east gales of recent years' was brewing. Soon huge waves were 'lashing the stricken battleship', swamping and smashing all but two of her lifeboats. She capsized and sank in less than two hours taking 547 men with her.

HMS Formidable

* In some newspaper reports there was no moon.

At about 11.00pm the following night Mr and Mrs Hardings and Gwen their daughter were walking home along the Marine Parade from dinner with friends. 'The seas were running very heavily and breaking at a great height upon the beach', Gwen recalled later. Suddenly they glimpsed an open boat making for the beach through the surf. There were 52 men aboard including six dead in the bottom of the boat. Of the 46 brought ashore alive, three died later. During their 22 hours in the freezing, sickening gale, fourteen more had been buried at sea.

How the boat found its way to Lyme Regis on the blacked-out coastline is not clear but one survivor, J H Taplin, reported that they saw a sudden bright light shine out while they were about three miles off. The projector at Mr Raymond's cinema in the Assembly Rooms' Victoria Hall had broken down that night and the light may well have been from the operator's lamp flashing through the bay window at the seaward end while he fiddled to fix the machine.

The Hardings raised the alarm and as the boat beached a crowd began to gather. The survivors were helped to the *Pilot Boat Inn* opposite the Assembly Rooms, where Mrs Atkins the landlady welcomed them in with hot coffee. 'I told her I would pay', reported Gwen Hardings later, 'but she would have none of it.'

One of the helpers tried but failed to summon a doctor by telephone, 'but the postmaster succeeded in putting me through to the Mayor'. Alban Woodroffe 'was speedily on the scene in his motor car, bringing with him a number of blankets which were very soon put to good effect. His Worship was indefatigable in his efforts to do everything for the men and, when they were temporarily clothed, he expeditiously conveyed them in his car to the cottage hospital and various hotels and private residences.'

Dr Cooper and Dr Spurr also soon appeared, doing what they could for the survivors including 'hypodermic injections of brandy and strychnine'.* The pub and later the entrance in the Assembly Rooms to the cinema were used as a mortuary. Boy-seaman Cowan was mistakenly laid out among the dead on the pub floor, but the landlady Mrs Atkins' dog Lassie drew attention to him by licking his face. The story made all the national newspapers and was the seed for the cinema legend, *Lassie*.

HMS Formidable funeral procession making its way to the service in the parish church.

*Strychnine – a popular poisonous plant-extract, also used in those days by doctors as a heart stimulant. Kill or cure.

6 WAR

The whole town turned out for the funeral. Later the Admiralty wrote to the council thanking Lyme Regis for all its help and hospitality. The council responded by resolving to charge the Admiralty for the burials at the 'resident' rather than the higher 'visitor' rate.

The hundreds of men lost with the *Formidable* affected everyone in town. At the end of January, to encourage its own young men 'to serve with the colours', the council hung boards outside the Guildhall, showing the names of all those who had already joined up. And in April it resolved 'to let it be known that when filling positions after the war, we intend to give preference to those who have served their country under arms or in making munitions of war'.

The *Formidable* disaster had increased everyone's awareness of the danger of attack from the sea so the council further reduced street lighting throughout the town. However, its request to the Dorset Electric Supply Co for a reduction in its contracted quarterly bill was rejected: the council's instruction not to light various public lights around the town was entirely its own affair. However, when in the summer the council decided to have no street lamps alight at all, it managed to persuade the Dorset Electric Supply Co to re-negotiate the original contract, and halve its annual payment from £240 to £120.

For the year to December 31st 1915, the Lyme Regis Electric Light Co's accounts show a profit of £651 12s.9d on sales of £919 15s.11d, but the profits of its owners, the County of Dorset Electric Supply Co, were falling: from £813 the previous year to just £388 16s.6d. According to the 1914-15 edition of *Garckes Manual*, the number of consumers in town had risen from 70 in 1913 to 87, and were now using a total of 1,561 light bulbs between them.

In January 1916 the House of Commons passed the Compulsory Service Bill. All fit single men in their 20s, so long as they were not in reserved occupations, would eventually be called up. Editorials thundered against 'slackers' and 'shirkers'. In February all the young men in Lyme Regis were ordered to report to Bridport on 3rd March to be registered and all the adult males in town of whatever age were from then on required to carry an identity card. The council published a Roll of Honour of the 254 men of the borough serving in His Majesty's forces.

At the end of the year, the *Daily Telegraph* ran a collection to provide Christmas puddings for the troops. In Lyme Regis it raised £4 15s.0d, including a guinea (£1 1s.0d) from Mr Woodroffe, two guineas from the Lyme freemasons and a shilling from 'Master Woodroffe', Alban's son Rex. For the year to 31st December 1916, the Electric Light Co's profits fell to just £24 8s.5d, while the County of Dorset Electric Supply Co made a loss of £72 8s.3d.

In January 1917, the *Bridport News* reported that 'all lads aged between 18 and 31', whether single or married, were now being conscripted, but reassured readers that none under 19 would be sent overseas. Nevertheless, the screw was tightening and the council was finding it increasingly difficult to get military exemption for its employees.

Food supplies and food production dominated the news. Under 'Nation's Food – Appeal for Voluntary Rations' the *Bridport News* announced that a voluntary rationing system was to be introduced: 4 lbs (1.8 kg) of bread per person per week, 2½ lbs of meat and ¾ lbs of sugar. And, the paper warned, if this voluntary appeal failed, the machinery for bringing a compulsory rationing system into operation was being got ready.

There was a National Egg Collecting Scheme. In Lyme Regis the local organiser Miss Bruce acknowledged receipt in January of the following gifts of eggs: Mrs Sharrard 24, Mrs Woodroffe 24, the Misses Preston nine, Mrs Cooper six, the parish of Charmouth 16 and that of Monkton Wylde ninety two. It looks as though Dr Cooper's wife was keeping hens up at Belmont along with her husband's pigs.

The council rented a ploughed field off the Sidmouth Road to the west of the town. The plan was to divide it into 64 plots, each large enough to plant a hundredweight (50kg) of seed potatoes, and let the plots to residents for 10 shillings a year.

The shortage of manpower and food was forcing prices up after decades of stability. Inflation in 1914 was -0.3 per cent , in 1915 12.5 per cent, and in 1916 18.1 per cent. In 1917 it reached 25.2 per cent. In February the council responded by raising its workmen's wages from 4¼d to 5d per hour, and those of its carters from £1 2s.0d to £1 4s.0d a week.

The sheer scale of the slaughter on the Western Front was kept from the people. *Pulman's Weekly* sometimes carried photos of the soldiers from local regiments killed in action, and the ominous phrase 'heavy casualties' appeared regularly; but the public only learned of the colossal losses after the war. For the time being in Lyme, what they knew was what they saw in its streets: a growing number of young women dressed in black, and older men with crumpled faces wearing mourning armbands.

On 25th February 1917 there was a memorial service at the parish church for four Lyme men killed in action in Mesopotamia, modern Iraq. Alban Wiscombe, Henry and Arthur Frost and George Hall had been serving with the Devonshire Regiment. The *Bridport News* told readers that reports from Axminster and along the coast suggested 'The Devons' had suffered heavy losses.

'A large congregation attended including many relatives of the deceased.' The service concluded with the National Anthem, 'which was sung by the congregation kneeling'. As they left the church, the muffled bells of St Michael's tolled out across the town. At the council meeting on 12th March, the members stood for a minute's silence in a show of sympathy for Alderman Wiscombe. He had lost his eldest son.

On 2nd March 1917 the *Bridport News* announced that Rhode Hill, 'the spacious and charming residence which His Worship the Mayor of Lyme Regis (Councillor A.J.Woodroffe) has placed at the disposal of the Red Cross authorities' was complete and ready to receive patients.

Rhode Hill in Edwardian days, before its conversion and use as a hospital.

The reporter was enthusiastic: 'The stately edifice, which is actually situated in the parish of Uplyme and about 1½ miles from Lyme Regis, occupies a glorious situation in a well-timbered park, looking across a lovely and heavily wooded valley, flanked by picturesque hills, to a wide expanse of sea.' He explained that Alban Woodroffe was personally bearing the expense of extensive alterations and redecoration to the building including a complete electric lighting plant installed by the Electric Light Company's resident engineer, Mr F.Cheshire. There were to be beds for 77 patients on three floors, a dining room, a recreation room, a billiard room, an operating theatre, a laundry and staff quarters.

The hospital had been open to supporters for inspection on the previous Thursday and to the general public on Sunday afternoon. 'The Mayor and Mayoress were present on both occasions to receive the visitors and assist them on their tour. A collecting box to provide funds for 'smokes' for the soldiers produced £2 17s.7½d on the first day and £7 1s. on Sunday.'

Patients and nurses at Rhode Hill. Alban Woodroffe, in uniform, is seated centre.

In April the secretary of Dorset's War Agricultural Committee wrote to the council about the need to grow as many potatoes as possible. They decided to buy a supply of seed potatoes and make them available to residents at minimal cost. Town Crier Walter Abbot would be employed to make the details known. Alban Woodroffe headed a committee to find another suitable field to let out for growing. At the end of the month news came that the seed potatoes had arrived at Yeovil Junction 25 miles away, and asking the council to arrange for their collection. As it did not yet have a motor lorry, the council would probably have sent over one of its own horses and carts, even if this had involved an overnight stop for the carter. Meanwhile the *Bridport News* carried a story headed, 'Huns Eating Cats'.

At the start of May the *Bridport News* had another story, 'Conscientious Objectors Mobbed in Lyme Regis'. It began, 'Scenes of the wildest excitement took place in the streets of the borough late on Friday night when a number of conscientious objectors, who, it was alleged, had jeered at the wounded soldiers in the town, were mobbed by an angry crowd. Since early in the year some 13 of these men have been occupied felling trees at St Mary's, an estate near Yawl. They have been in the habit of spending some of their leisure evenings in the borough and, although their visits have never been appreciated, they were in no way molested up to the occurrence in question.'

The report explained that half a dozen of the men had got into conversation during the afternoon with some wounded soldiers from the Rhode Hill Hospital who were on the Marine Parade, and were alleged to have jeered at the soldiers 'for doing their bit'. A crowd gathered and were 'very annoyed with the attitude taken up by the conscience men'. Later in the evening, when the men were sitting on the sea wall at Cobb Gate, 'a number of people gathered for an exchange of views. A general scrimmage ensued and one of the men was in grave danger of being thrown into the sea by a woman, but was rescued in the nick of time by someone seizing his legs. The crowd, which subsequently assumed considerable dimensions, and included a large number of women and girls, commenced shortly after dusk to round up such of the men as had not already cleared out of the town.'

Two men had to be rescued from the crowd by Sergeant Stockley and Police Constable Stanley, and two more were besieged in a restaurant and escaped over a back wall and across several gardens. 'No damage was done to the restaurant except that the entrance door showed considerable signs of boot marks.' A last man, who had been for a walk with a young lady, turned up at about 10.30, and was 'somewhat hustled, lectured by a soldier and marched up the street, but the police on arrival affected his liberation and the crowd dispersed'.

More and more men were being drawn away to the war. In the spring, despite councillors' attempts to dissuade him, Town Clerk Ramsbotham tendered his resignation and joined up. In June the papers reported that a young lady had been thrown from her trap in Broad Street when her horse slipped, and had been 'injured considerably'. They put the accident down to two council roadworkers, Mr Hallett and Mr Stone, being called up. They had been 'engaged in cracking gravel' to make the roads less slippery. At about the same time the council was informed that the blacksmith's assistant who shoed the council's heavy horses had also been conscripted.

The perennial problem of Lyme's water supply reappeared in the summer of 1917. Councillor Camplin, whose interest in the problem extended over decades, complained that the shortage was made worse because the street-watering cart was being filled from the mains hydrants instead of with water from the river pumped by the Electric Light Co's electric pump. Surveyor McDonnell explained that the pump had been broken since last autumn, and wartime shortages meant they had only now managed to get spare parts.

Another shortage was newsprint, which was gradually reducing the size of newspapers. The *Bridport News* was down to four pages although it could still find space to run a story about starvation in Germany.

In November the council passed a vote of sympathy for former-mayor Bickley and his wife on the news of the death in action of their youngest son George, aged 25. Captain Bickley, and also Captain Powell, the deputy-head of the National School, had been killed in October during the advance on Passchendaele. Eight years earlier, the Bickleys' daughter Beatrice had died of meningitis at the age of 21 in Dresden in Germany. Her body had been returned by train for burial in Lyme, 'enclosed in a metallic shell with outer oak coffin - white plated fittings', via Liverpool Street and Axminster stations. Her brother George's remains were buried along with nearly 12,000 others at the Tyne Cot cemetery in Belgium, the largest Commonwealth War Grave in the world.

Tyne Cot Cemetery near Ypres

By the end of 1917 the police considered it safe for certain street lamps to be re-lit, providing they could not be seen from the sea and were 'obscured in the manner required by the Chief Constable'. The Deputy Town Clerk submitted a list of 22 lamps for re-lighting to Superintendent Saint who despatched Sergeant Stockley off to inspect. He reported that five might still be spotted from the sea so the list was cut to seventeen. The Clerk wrote to the Electric Light Co asking them to turn the select few back on.

In 1917 the Electric Light Co made a loss of £107 1s.11d and the Dorset Electric Supply Co one of £974 12s.11d. The loss in Lyme Regis seems in part to have been due to an enormous rise in the cost of fuel oil. The 1916 accounts show the total cost of generating the town's electricity as £309, including £137 for fuel and £77 for wages. In 1917 the cost of fuel oil alone came to £419.

From mid-1917 there had been regular Zeppelin and bomber attacks on southern England and at the start of 1918 the government encouraged coastal towns to introduce air-raid precautions. In mid-January Alban Woodroffe informed his fellow councillors that 'it has been arranged with the Chief Constable that the air-raid warning for the Borough will, if required, be given by the Town Crier Mr Walter Abbott, who will ring his bell and call, "Take cover!".'

Despite the threat from the air, the 17 street lamps approved by Sergeant Stockley in December were now alight and the council asked the County of Dorset Electric Supply Co whether they would supply the current for lighting them at no extra cost. After all, they had been paying a standing charge of £120 a year since July 1915 for no street lighting at all.

In January 1918 the company replied. 'The Board duly noted your suggestion that current for these lamps be supplied free of charge in view of the payment you are at present making under your contract. I am instructed, however, courteously to point out that this payment was agreed by your council as an amount to repay us in respect of outlay on capital and other expenses incurred by us under the suspended contract. However the Company, purely as a matter of goodwill, is willing to supply current for the 17 lamps in question without charge until August 31st when the matter can again be gone into. However, my Company is at the moment faced with a great difficulty in getting adequate supplies of fuel oil. Our proposal therefore depends on our oil merchants maintaining supply. Yours etc. T.W. Cole. Secretary.'

Now there were also widespread shortages of food, with complaints in the local papers about the exorbitant price of milk and meat and accusations that local tradesmen were profiteering. The seriousness of the situation can be judged by the 'Horse Rationing Order' introduced by the government in May. This restricted the amount that horses could be given to eat. In Lyme Regis the council sent the corporation cart off around the town to find whatever feed it could for the local pigs.

What rubbish could not be fed to pigs found its way to the council's rubbish dump or 'scavenging heap', located downwind to the east of the town on a field above the cliffs. In the spring the Admiralty complained that it was on fire, and that enemy shipping might use it at night for navigation. Could the flames be hidden behind a screen? Sergeant Stockley was sent off to inspect and reported back that the screen idea was impractical. The council adopted an alternative plan: the fire was allowed to burn itself out.

In July the council agreed to adopt a resolution sent in by a London lady demanding 'the immediate internment of all aliens of enemy <u>blood</u> [her underlining], whether naturalised or unnaturalised'. It is unlikely anyone of 'enemy <u>blood</u>' in Lyme Regis was affected. The Allhusens at Pinhay were originally from Germany, but then so was the Royal Family. However, the resolution indicates the bitterness people were now feeling.

August saw the fourth anniversary of the start of a war that many had expected would be over by the first Christmas. The *Bridport News* appealed for volunteers to work in the kitchens at Alban Woodroffe's Rhode Hill hospital. It suggested that summer visitors to the town might be willing 'to devote some portion of their leisure to this useful and patriotic work'. In the same month the council put in a request for exemption from military service for Mr Fowler, Lyme's chimney sweep. Unswept chimneys posed a serious fire hazard to the town. Ironically, the reply rejecting the request arrived on Armistice Day in November. Mr Fowler was called up and remained in the forces until general demobilisation the following year.

In September 1918 Mayor Woodroffe informed his fellow councillors that on the previous evening, despite being attended by a veterinary surgeon, the council's best horse had died. They decide to buy a middle-of-the-range replacement offered by local farmer Shirley Jenks of Herne Lee for £120, but later changed their mind and bought a better one from Mr Hawkings for £150. To put this price in context, following their 1917 pay-rise to 5d an hour, council labourers in Lyme Regis were now paid £1 for a 48-hour week, so this new horse cost about three years' wages.

In the summer and autumn of 1918, the devastating 'Spanish Flu' epidemic (known understandably in Spain as 'French Flu') swept across Europe, killing more people than all those lost on its battlefields. In Britain 228,000 died, with nearly 7,500 in just the first week in November. In Lyme Regis, Medical Officer of Health Dr Spurr reported that 'a large number of children were stricken down with the malady' but that there had only been one death. The schools were closed for a fortnight.

On 11th November the Armistice was signed. On the war memorial in George's Square the names of 59 men who fought and died for King and country appear, a grievous loss for the little town. Up the river in Uplyme a further 28 would never come home.

CREAKING SEAMS

Before striding purposefully into the 1920s, it is worth a pause to take stock. At the end of the First World War the population of the UK was 44 million compared with 60 million today. 4,200,000 men had served in the forces, mainly in the army, and 744,000 had been killed: chilling odds of 1:6. (In the Second World War the odds had lengthened to 1:17.)

The average British family had just over three children compared with only 1.7 in 1997. Infant mortality was about 80 per thousand births whereas now it has dropped to less than six per thousand. In 1918, even excluding the terrible effects of the war and the Spanish Flu epidemic, the average life expectancy of a new-born boy was about 52 and a girl to 55. Today a boy can expect to live to 75 years, and a girl to about eighty. In those days 90 per cent of the population lived in rented accommodation. Now the figure is 30 per cent.

At the start of 1919, the Secretary of State for War Mr Winston Churchill announced a demobilisation plan for the millions of troops. Those who had served longest or 'been wounded more often' would be home first. However, the England they returned to was one of shortages, scarce jobs and shockingly high prices. Inflation had run at 25 per cent in 1916/17 and 22 per cent in 1917/18, and wages had not kept pace. There was a temporary post-war boom, but then unemployment started to soar and through much of the 1920s and 1930s prices, and in some cases wages, actually fell.

In matters electrical, the number of British homes with electricity had risen from fewer than 2 per cent in 1910 to about 6 per cent at the end of the First World War. Virtually all these half million homes were in larger towns and cities: if you lived in a village or the country you lit your home as your grandparents had with oil lamps and candles. Even where there was a supply, electricity was still confined to the rich: gas was cheaper.*

Almost all domestic electricity was used for lighting. The first cookers, kettles and irons were just beginning to appear at prices the middle classes could afford, but it would not be until well after the Second World War that fridges and washing machines arrived in ordinary homes. For most families, a solid-fuel range in the kitchen remained the typical means of cooking food and heating water until the 1950s.

Electric kettle c. 1919.

*Even in the 1930s, the cost of heating with electricity was about twice as much as with gas & four times as much as coal.

43

7 CREAKING SEAMS

As most private consumers still used electricity only for lighting at night, electricity companies had spare generating capacity sitting idle during the day. It made clear commercial sense to persuade consumers to use up this spare daytime electricity for heating and lighting. Many companies therefore introduced a two-part tariff, with a much cheaper 'power-rate' for non-lighting purposes and their higher lighting rate. To take advantage of the power rate, houses needed to be wired with separate power circuits and meters, but it was priced to make it nevertheless an attractive proposition.

The cost of electricity in real terms was at least three times that of today, and far more than that in a small town like Lyme Regis where there were no economies of scale. Prices varied a good deal from town to town, as did voltage, frequency and type of current: AC or DC. A national standard had yet to be agreed. When a new public electricity supply appeared, its technical specifications often depended on the personal experience and preferences of the engineer who happened to have been given the job of installing it.

In Lyme Regis the number of electricity consumers had risen, despite the war, from 87 in 1914 to 133 in 1918. These will have included better-off private homes and the town's leading shops, offices and hotels. The average number of light bulbs per consumer had increased from about seventeen to twenty-five. By 1920 the cost of a unit of electricity had doubled from 6d in 1909 to a shilling; but as prices generally had gone up two and a half times since 1910, in real terms electricity was getting cheaper.

However, for the Lyme Regis Electric Light and Power Company Ltd, the position in 1919 was not happy. It had made another loss in 1918, of £53 4s.1d. Its original equipment was already a decade old and beginning to show its age. And the fact that, despite a national fuel shortage, the Company was allowed to re-light half the town's street lamps had only gone to draw attention that many of them were not working very well.

At about this time a new resident electrical engineer, Arthur Brown, joined the company. A former warrant officer in the Royal Navy, he had learned his trade over more than thirty years at sea, going back to the days of wooden ships and almost the start of practical electricity. Arthur and Mrs Brown now moved into the Engineer's House at 5a Coombe Street, sometimes charmingly referred to as 'Electricity Cottage'. On the ground floor was the company's office, opening straight onto the street. Directly behind was the Malthouse generating station. Arthur was to shepherd Lyme Regis's electricity supply through most of the next thirty years, almost to the eve of nationalisation.

In March 1919 Mayor Woodroffe reminded the council that its ten-year street-lighting contract with the Electric Light & Power Co was due to expire on 1st June. The Highways Committee was told to draw up a new one, but this time there was no question of a long-term contract, there were signs that the system was failing, and anyway the original need to entice potential investors with that level of guarantee had long disappeared.

In May, the committee returned with its proposal for a new 12-month contract to 1st June 1920. If the council agreed, 16 of the town's 90 street lamps would be fairly bright with 100-watt bulbs at a cost of £5-10-0 per lamp per year, while the remaining 80 would be pretty dim 30-watt lamps at £3-10-0 each per year. The annual bill would be £368. The council did not agree: this plan would leave the streets extravagantly bright. Ten of the 100-watt lamps were downgraded to 30 watts, leaving just six fairly bright 100-watt lamps in town but saving the ratepayers £20 a year.

At the end of the summer of 1919, a Lighting Vehicles Order came into force making it compulsory for all vehicles, horse-drawn or motor, to carry a red light at the rear at night.

Sergeant Stockley retired from the Lyme police after nearly 30 years' service, and a charity dance for the local hospice for the blind was held in the Assembly Rooms.

There was also a complaint that the Marine Parade was not being properly lit so Borough Surveyor Major McDonnell* was instructed to keep a tally of the 'lamps out'. (In the new contract the penalty for a lamp out had been raised from 2d to 3d per day.) In October Major MacDonnell reported back: there had been 174 lamps out since the start of September. Town Clerk Ramsbotham wrote to the company drawing their attention to 'the very unsatisfactory state of public lighting'.

In November Alban Woodroffe, now 45, was appointed High Sheriff of Dorset. After ten years as a councillor and five as mayor, he handed his chain of office over to Alderman Alben Wiscombe and left the borough council. He remained, however, a director of the Electric Light Co's owners, the County of Dorset Electric Supply Co, and they now wrote regretting the state of Lyme's street lighting and saying they had instructed their consulting engineer, Mr Ingram, to take immediate action.

A very brief improvement in the system did not last. At Christmas 1919 there was a general breakdown in street lighting, and the whole town centre was plunged into darkness. In a report to the council, Engineer Ingram explained that the failure was due to a breakdown in the insulation of the underground cables: those bare wires laid ten years earlier in pitch-filled troughs.

So ended 1919, the year when Nancy Astor became the first woman MP, Alcock and Brown flew the Atlantic and the County of Dorset Electric Supply Co managed to make a loss of £3,086 15s.4d.

In spring 1920, Major McDonnell reported on 'the very unsatisfactory state of public lighting since the Armistice' Just from the start of February to the end of April that year, he told councillors he had counted a total of 1,212 lamps out and, he added, 'other lamps, even when supposed to be lit, give practically no illumination'.

The council resolved not to pay the company anything for that quarter. The new one-year contract would finish at the end of May and Town Clerk Ramsbotham was told to write 'protesting in the strongest possible terms' and saying the council would have to consider 'other means of lighting'. (This sounds a bit of an empty threat: they had got rid of all the redundant gas lamps and could not seriously have contemplated lighting the streets with oil lamps or flaming torches.)

The company protested. 'No pains or expense are being spared to make good the defects', they said. A considerable amount of new cable was being laid, and new feeder-cables fitted for the overhead lines. Indeed the necessary materials had been ordered a considerable time before, but because of shortages and delays etc, etc.

In May the new materials were delivered and the company promised that public lighting would be in good order by the end of the month. It offered the council a new contract for the coming year but, most regrettably, there would have to be a price increase of £53. However, to demonstrate its confidence in the repairs, the company would increase the penalty it paid for each lamp out from 3d to 8d per day. Can't say fairer than that. The council accepted but with one tiny amendment: to offset the price increase they would not bother with any street lighting at all in July and August.

---

* Mr Frederick McDonnell, Borough Surveyor, Engineer, Sanitary Inspector and Inspector of Common Lodging Houses, worked for the council before and during the war. Quite how he suddenly got promoted to Major remains unexplained.

To work out how much this would save, the company produced a complicated calculation based on the streets being lit for a total of 1,434 hours a year, or an average of 3.93 hours a night. Moonlit nights and longer summer evenings were also factored in. The bottom line was that having zero street lights in July and August would save the ratepayers £26 a year.

The other matter to be resolved was that because it had been so cross about the unreliability of the supply, the council had not paid for any electricity at all for the last seven months. About £200 was due. However, by making deductions for all the lamps out and also charging the company for repairing the roads dug up to lay new cables, the council whittled the final bill down to £91 8s.5d.

In the autumn, there was disagreement between the council and the company on whether the lights worked on 4th September. However, for the night of 7th October the company was forced to admit that for two hours there had been total darkness in the town.

The County of Dorset Electric Supply Co was now keen to get rid of its Lyme Regis subsidiary. The Electric Light Co made a loss of £274 in 1920. Its other electricity undertakings in Blandford, Dorchester, Sherborne, Swanage and Wimborne were doing badly too. The group accounts for 1920 show a 'balance at debit thereof' of £3,980 16s.7½d. There is also mention of 'a loan, secured by 5% debenture on personal guarantee, and interest thereon, of £13,689 8s.10d.' That was a very large debt.

8
TAKEOVER

On 13th September 1920 the council adopted a slightly startling motion: 'That it is desirable that all undertakings of Public Utility be under the direct control of the Council, and that the mayor be empowered to enter into any negotiations to that end.'

No sane person ever accused Lyme Regis Borough Council of left-wing tendencies but, on the face of it, doesn't this sound slightly Socialist?

The truth was that a battle was brewing within the council about whether or not to buy the Electric Light & Power Co. The motion was probably bounced through to establish the general principle. And what lay behind it was no brave new political ideology but that same sense of civic responsibility and pride that inspired Victorian city fathers to give England its town hall clocks, public parks, libraries and municipal baths (for washing, not swimming).

In any event, a couple of days later Mr Shirley Jenks, the farmer who had not quite managed to sell the council a horse when its best one died two years before, wrote to Mayor Wiscombe. What made Jenks do so is not clear, but he obviously had some electrical expertise.

Jenks told the mayor he had inspected the Electric Light Co's plant that morning, and in his view 'the whole of the plant is absolutely useless excepting as a stand-by, and the 140 subscribers need new cables.' He thought the premises and present equipment might be worth up to £1,000. To buy and then completely re-equip the Malthouse would, he considered, cost eight to nine thousand pounds. And if the mayor were interested, Mr Jenks' advice was to 'sell more current at a less price than a small amount at a very high figure'.

Mr Jenks must have also contacted the County of Dorset Electric Supply Co because at the end of the month Engineer Ingram wrote to Jenks detailing (in as positive terms as possible) their subsidiary's assets. Here was the first comprehensive picture of how the Lyme Regis Electric Light & Power Co was equipped. (The details eventually found their way to the Dorset County Records Office, to be filed in a box marked 'Water'.) If you have no interest in technical matters you may safely skip the next four paragraphs.

The assets now included two generating sets in the Malthouse. One was the original 35 HP Gardner oil engine driving a 21½kW dynamo, and there was a second 25 HP Gardner (described elsewhere as a 'horizontal paraffin engine') driving an 18kW dynamo. Ingram went on, 'There is also a 40 HP producer gas engine (elsewhere described as a 'suction gas engine') with dynamo and switchboard etc, but this is not in operation owing to the unsuitability of the engine. It is not the property of the Company, but on hire.'

In addition in the Malthouse was a 64-cell chloride battery accumulator, switchboards and connections. There is no record of when the second Gardner engine or the battery accumulator were installed, but in all probability the battery appeared very early on in the company's career because one of the great advantages of a DC system is that you can store electricity in a battery at one time for use at another. With an AC system you can't do this.

The assets also included 'the freehold of the works and the dwelling house attached': the Malthouse and Engineer Brown's house at 5a Coombe Street, 'Electricity Cottage'.

The two Gardner generating sets in the Malthouse before it was re-equipped in 1924.

The report continues, 'The mains are laid on the two-wire system, with a declared pressure of 110 volts. There are approximately 1,500 yards laid underground and 6,500 yards overhead. The number of consumers is 144, of which nine have been connected in the first part of this year. Also in the last year, the number of street lamps, about 20 of which are cast iron standards, has increased from 90 to 97.'

Turning to the subject of the water turbine at Higher Mill, Engineer Ingram explains, 'There is also, not at the works, a 5kW Crompton Dynamo driven by a 7½ HP Gilkes Water Turbine and belt. The water rights are held at a very low annual rental and are of considerable value as the water-power plant carries the whole of the load after midnight till the following evening for the greater part of the year. With the battery in good order, it would enable the works to be shut down for two or three days a week in the summer, materially reducing the cost of operation.'

Things went quiet for a few weeks. Then in November 1920 council minutes record, 'A public meeting was held at the Town Hall a short time ago in consequence to complaints as to the inefficiency of the electric lighting.' Evidently Lyme's electricity supply had deteriorated to a point where the drawing rooms and parlours throughout the town were abuzz with indignation. 'What in the name of boiling hell is the point of getting your house all wired up for this electric light thingy when you spend half your time groping around in the dark and falling down stairs?'

The public meeting was alarming. Might it be just the first step towards a mob howling for the head of the mayor? In St Petersburg, recently renamed Leningrad, possibly; but surely not in Lyme Regis. Instead, the meeting appointed a Consumer Council, headed by a prominent private resident, the Reverend G.F.Eyre, 'to see what steps might be taken in the matter of purchasing the electricity company'.

8 TAKEOVER

Spurred into action, on 12th November the council considered whether to accept an offer from the Dorset Electric Supply Co to sell it the Electric Light Co for £4,500. Alban Woodroffe told them the option would remain open for just 14 days. This was clearly decision-time, so the council resolved to ask Shirley Jenks if he might suggest an engineer to possibly conduct a survey and write a report on the state of the electricity system for not more than £75.

Alban's ruse to get the council moving with his 14-day deadline had obviously failed, so next day he wrote again saying he understood, 'that last evening the council did not decide to buy the Lyme Regis Electric Light and Power Company, even if their engineer's report was favourable, and so, under the circumstances, I have given the other interested person the option to purchase.'

The other interested person turned out to be Shirley Jenks himself. He apparently planned to buy the company, break it up and sell off the bits. In fact this did not make a great deal of sense as in September Jenks had said he thought the company's 'premises and present equipment might be worth up to £1,000'. He was hardly likely to pay £4,500 for them now. Another possibility was that a conversation along the following lines had taken place earlier between Alban and Shirley.

- Hello, Jenks. I hope you're well.
- Can't complain Mr Woodroffe, sir.
- Good man. Good man. That's what I like to hear.
- If you don't mind me saying so Mr Woodroffe, you're looking a bit thoughtful.
- Oh, the electricity company, you mean?
- Is there anything I can do for you, sir? I'll never forget the way you saved me from that anaconda in South America back in '98. And the head-hunters, sir.
- Happy days. Ah yes! Happy days! But now you come to mention it, there is something you could do.
- Just say the word, sir. You know me.
- Jenks, I need someone to seem interested in buying the electricity company.
- Well, the council is, isn't it sir?
- Yes, at least allegedly. But someone else. A bit of interest. A bit of competition. You see, Jenks, between you and me, its system is totally out of date and its infrastructure is on the verge of collapse. I speak of course of the electricity company, not the council.
- Naturally, Mr Woodroffe.
- So, Jenks, what I'd like you to do is pretend you're interested in buying the company. Start making overtures. It might encourage our friends in the Guildhall to take action. Like jealous lovers, if you see what I mean.
- If you think they'll buy it, Mr Woodroffe.
- Fingers crossed, Jenks. I can't see anyone else who will.

Whatever the truth behind the scenes, Jenks shortly afterwards teamed up with the council, jointly to get to an engineer's valuation of the company at the council's expense. The engineer Jenks found was a Mr Tilley, who reported to the mayor just before Christmas that he valued the company at £3,869, but that a further £5,895 would be needed for new equipment and cables. The total cost would thus be just short of £10,000. Tilley also said that if electricity output and sales were increased by 60 per cent, the annual revenue would rise to £3,500 and make the undertaking a profit of £865 a year.

8 TAKEOVER

At about this time Alban Woodroffe wrote to Jenks again, offering to sell the Electric Light Co either to him or to the council for £4,250, the option again open for just 14 days.

Just before Christmas eight members of the new Electricity Consumers' Council led by the Reverend Eyre attended the council meeting. They announced they could raise the £10,000 needed for the council to buy the Electric Light Co, and charge them only six or seven per cent interest. The council then voted: they resolved to buy the Electric Light Co for £4,250, subject to due safeguards and the necessary loan. An amendment by more cautious councillors to offer only £3,000 was defeated by seven votes to four.

In February 1921, a group of councillors led by Surveyor McDonnell trooped round the town one evening to inspect the 'ineffective public lighting', and then discussed whether to put the plan of buying the electricity company to a referendum of the ratepayers. This idea was felt to be taking democracy a step too far and was defeated by five votes to two.

Up in London a firm of solicitors called Barlow, Barlow and Lyde acted as the council's parliamentary agents. They had been investigating the legal implications of its buying an electricity company. In March they wrote explaining it would be illegal for the council to borrow money against the security of the rates – if things all went horribly wrong the ratepayers would ultimately be liable – unless it first got approval from what Barlows mistakenly called the 'Electric Commissioners'.

The Electricity Commissioners was a statutory national body formed in January 1920 to supervise the industry. Its jobs included giving the private and municipal electricity companies permission to increase their prices, approving their engineering standards and sanctioning their loans. For Lyme Regis that meant that before the council could legally borrow the money to buy and re-equip the Electric Light Co, it first had to satisfy the Commissioners that the scheme made both technical and financial sense.

The Commissioners had seen Engineer Tilley's report but now wanted more technical details and also to know what Mr Tilley's qualifications were. 'Who's this fellow Tilley? Never heard of him.' It transpired that Tilley's qualifications fell short of the Commissioners' requirements but he recommended a colleague, Mr R.W.Weekes, who was a fully paid-up Member of the Institution of Electrical Engineers. MIEE was the industry gold-standard, and Mr Weekes MIEE agreed to undertake a survey and valuation of the Electric Light Co for a fee of seven guineas a day plus out of pocket travelling expenses.

In his preliminary report in early June, Mr Weekes said it was essential that more space was available for future expansion of the generating station. The mayor undertook to have an informal chat with local landlord Edwin Wallis. He owned number 5 Coombe Street, the house next to Engineer Brown's house, whose garden adjoined the Malthouse. Mayor Wiscombe reported back that Wallis was willing to sell them the house for £400.

In August Weekes reported that 'the present plant and mains are practically valueless' and estimated the total capital required would be £11,700. At the same time Barlow, Barlow and Lyde advised the council to pay the Dorset Electric Supply Co the £4,250 they had agreed for the company not in cash but in Corporation Bonds. 'It seems to us that the Company would be bound to accept these terms as, so far as we know, they are not in the least likely to find a purchaser elsewhere.'

As Christmas 1921 approached, the board of the County of Dorset Electric Supply Co had no option but to extend the deadline for the sale. However, they made it perfectly clear they were not prepared to take one penny less than £4,250 in cash for the Electric Light Co.

8 TAKEOVER

1922 came and went without the sale complete. The council was now contracted to buying the electricity undertaking, but subject to the Electricity Commissioners approving the terms of its deal with the Dorset Electrical Supply Co. Its only electrical achievement in the year was to buy the house and garden at 5 Coombe Street from Mr Wallis for the agreed £400.

———•———

Elsewhere in the town the council offered a £2 reward for information leading to the conviction of the person or persons who had been throwing stones at the increasingly dim street lamps along the Marine Parade. The council's oldest horse had fallen down at work so it was sold off to Farmer Harris at Ware for £5. And Alderman and Ex-Mayor Sam Harris went off with Councillor Hynes to inspect a six-ton rick of hay, which Farmer Love then sold the Council for £40.

In January 1923 the council horses' oat ration was increased from eight to twelve pecks each per week 'when engaged in gravel hauling or watering the roads'. A peck is about nine litres. Their poor condition was blamed on a delivery of inferior hay.

In February, the council received a claim for the cost of repairing a motorcycle combination belonging to Mr Potts of Bridport. The repairs cost £6 5s.9d and were, said the insurance company, 'entirely due to insufficient lighting while the road was up'. Apparently, the council had marked the road works by suspending a single small red light in front of them 'a short distance from the ground'. Mr Potts mistook this for one of the new-fangled rear lights introduced in 1919, swerved to avoid it and overturned his machine. At first the council denied any liability – its standard tactic – but when pressed further offered £5 without prejudice in full settlement. Meanwhile in Cambridge, according to the *Bridport News*, Sir Ernest Rutherford was firing particles of helium in his laboratory at a speed of 10,000 miles a second in an effort to break up the atom.

———•———

The purchase of the Electric Light Co dragged on. The council and the County of Dorset Electricity Supply Company now agreed on their latest not-one-penny-less price of £3,750. However, the Electricity Commissioners said that this was still too much and proposed £3,000. In May 1923 a compromise was reached at £3,400 and the council arranged with the manager at Lloyds Bank in Axminster to borrow the money from them. On 16th July 1923 Parliament approved the purchase order and the deal was done.

The sale more or less coincided with the demise of the County of Dorset Electric Supply Co. Its accounts to the end of 1922 showed 'Amount spent on Dorchester undertaking: £13,537 13s.11½d. Amount received from the Borough of Dorchester for sale: £9,034 0s.0d. Loss: £4,503 13s.11½d'. The company's total loss for that year was £5,299 18s.6½d.

Dorchester had been the jewel in the Dorset Electric Supply Co's crown. At about that time it appears to have also sold off its Sherborne, Blandford and Wimborne undertakings, since the banner on its letterhead in spring 1923 boasted only 'Supplying Electricity at Lyme Regis and Swanage'. Its accounts to December 1923 show a total debt due of £5,792 6s.6d - equivalent in those days to the cost of building a dozen council houses. At a board meeting in January 1924, Alban Woodroffe, Dr Hosker and the other directors voted to appoint a liquidator to wind the company up.

MAKEOVER

Thus it came to pass that in the summer of 1923, Lyme Regis Borough Council found itself the owner of a clapped out electricity company with all the considerable statutory powers and obligations Parliament had decided such ownership entailed.

The town's electricity supply had by this time literally become a bit of a joke. When in June a lawyer in the County Court at nearby Axminster confessed he had never seen 'the electric light works in Lyme Regis', Mayor Ellis interjected to general laughter, 'You can't even see the electric light sometimes!'

Mayor Henry Ellis

The case before His Honour Judge the Hon.W.B.Lindlay concerned number 5 Coombe Street, the house next to 'Electricity Cottage'. The council had bought it from Edwin Wallis the previous year because its garden, which adjoined the so-called electric light works in the Malthouse, offered space for expansion.

A gardener called Tom Stoodley lived in the house with his wife and grown-up daughter. The council wanted them out. It had issued them with a notice to quit the April before and had offered an alternative house, but the family was resisting because they said the new house was too small.

Town Clerk Ramsbotham told the judge that the only reason the council had bought the house in the first place was because they wanted to enlarge and improve the electricity works. At present the sole access to the Malthouse was across the old bridge in Mill Lane, and this was not strong enough for heavy traffic. They planned to create new access to the works direct from Coombe Street through the Stoodley's garden but, sadly, to do this part of the house and the Stoodleys would have to be removed.

Judge Lindley asked what the Stoodley's present and proposed houses comprised. Number 5 Coombe Street had two sitting rooms, a kitchen, a scullery and a small room used as an extra bedroom on the ground floor. Upstairs were four more bedrooms. There was no mention of a bathroom but the house must at least have had a WC, probably in the large garden at the back. (Although it was built directly over the river, the days of WCs emptying straight into the Lym ended, at least in theory, in 1903 when the borough laid new sewers 'to convey sewage directly into the sea'.) The Stoodley's rent for the house was 10s.11d a week.

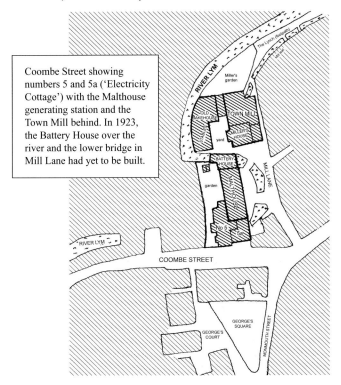

Coombe Street showing numbers 5 and 5a ('Electricity Cottage') with the Malthouse generating station and the Town Mill behind. In 1923, the Battery House over the river and the lower bridge in Mill Lane had yet to be built.

In its place the council was offering them one of its small stock of council houses, in nearby Corporation Terrace. That house consisted of a sitting room, a kitchen, a scullery and a larder on the ground floor, three bedrooms on the first floor and a small garden, all for 8s.1d a week.

The Stoodley's lawyer, Mr Saunders from Crewkerne, explained that Mrs Stoodley regularly took in up to five lodgers all year round, and that the three bedrooms and sitting room she let out had already been booked until mid-September. 'The alternative accommodation would deprive Mrs Stoodley of part of her livelihood,' thundered Mr Saunders.

Judge Lindlay said that the Corporation had to satisfy the court that the alternative accommodation was reasonably equivalent and suitable in all respects. The letting of rooms was part of the livelihood of the tenant. He found in favour of the Stoodleys and awarded them costs. The council abandoned its plan and instead strengthened the bridge in Mill Lane. Number 5 remained the Stoodleys' home for another quarter century.

Back in 1921 to satisfy the Electricity Commissioners, Consulting Engineer Weekes from Bournemouth had drawn up plans to convert the town from a 110-volt DC 2-wire system to a 440-volt DC 3-wire system. (These rather alarming 440 volts would normally be split for domestic consumers to deliver 220 volts per household.) The council now employed Weekes, for a fee of £500 plus five per cent of the cost of any extras, to put his scheme into effect.

At present in the Malthouse there were the two ageing generating sets which between them could produce just under 40kW, and the worn-out 64-cell battery. Up at Higher Mill there was the 7½ HP Gilkes water turbine driving a 5kW Crompton Dynamo.

In place of these Weekes planned to install a new 50kW diesel generating set and keep the larger of the original Gardner horizontal paraffin engines to drive a new 20kW dynamo. These would almost double the Malthouse generating capacity to 70kWs. Up at Higher Mill, Mr Caddy was not sure he would be allowed to lease out the water power again – a shadowy figure he referred to as 'the Lieutenant' needed to give his approval – so the water turbine was written out of the scheme.

Weekes also specified a brand new 264-cell battery accumulator for storing current: imagine 264 car batteries all linked together in rows. These would stand in ranks on the floor of a bright new red brick battery-house he planned to tack onto the end of the historic stone Malthouse. The changeover to the 440-volt system would begin with the construction of the battery house.

The first plan was to build the battery-house at right angles to the Malthouse, along the river bank, but this would have involved building on a bit of land owned by Mr Geake the dentist. Then in August 1923 the council suddenly realised it would cost only £60 more to build the battery house over the river, and then they would not need to buy bits of land from Mr Geake or anyone else.

A slight problem was that the Town Mill owned the rights to the riverbed and anything above it. Back in 1912 Edwin Wallis had sold the Mill to W.H.Pinney & Co, a coal and general merchant from Axminster. William Pinney had installed his stepson Oswald Fowler in the miller's house to grind the mill in its final years, and run his coal business from its yard. However, Pinney and Fowler were accommodating fellows and they agreed to let the council build over the river in return for letting them widen the entrance into their yard by two feet.

Oswald Fowler, the last miller, with his wife and son Robert in the Town Mill garden in about 1922.

9 MAKEOVER

Plan for the re-equipped Malthouse by Engineer Weekes, showing the belt-driven and free-standing generating sets, cooling water and fuel tanks, the underground exhaust silencing-pit for the new engine, and the new battery-house with its banks of accumulators.

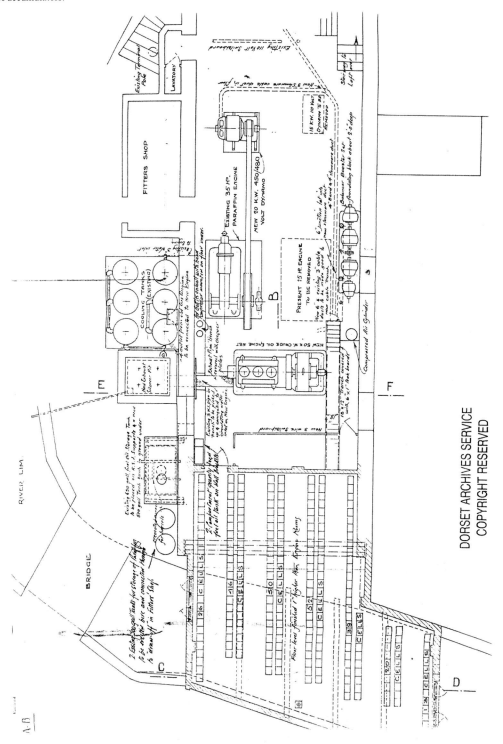

9 MAKEOVER

In the autumn of 1923 the council advertised in *Pulman's Weekly* for tenders to build the new battery house. Mr R.G.Spiller of Chard won with a quote of £782. The battery house, however, was just the first stage in the voltage changeover. While it was being built and until the new generating equipment was installed, consumers would have to put up with the present unreliable supply of electricity and, most important for the council's budget, keep on paying for it. In December the council circulated a fierce warning that unless their overdue accounts were paid, consumers were liable to be cut off.

When the council took over the Electric Light Co, it also inherited from the private company Arthur Brown, its engineer. He now became the Borough Electrical Engineer, responsible to the council for managing its new Electricity Department. They evidently trusted him as they authorised him to draw cheques of up to £10 for wages on the Department's account at Lloyds Bank. Because of inflation, wages had soared over the previous six years, and Mr Weekes had estimated that by 1924 a skilled worker like a fitter or wireman would be earning 2s.6d an hour or £6 for a 48-hour week, a bricklayer 2s.4d, a painter 2s.3d and even a labourer would get 1s.9d an hour or £4 4s.0d a week. In fact, depending on your point of view, this was wildly optimistic or pessimistic. Wage-levels in West Dorset were well below the national average and, anyway, the sharp wage and price rises after the war were now firmly in reverse, and would continue to fall well into the 1930s.

Elsewhere in Lyme there was progress in education. One of the voluntary positions Alban Woodroffe had taken on when he first joined the council in 1909 was that of 'School Manager of the Lyme Regis Public Elementary School'. This Victorian national school, with its separate entrances for Boys, Girls and Infants, provided compulsory education from age five to twelve for the town's children.   In 1914, the National School inspectors complained that the children did not know their multiplication tables. In 1921, the Education Act raised the Minimum School Leaving Age from twelve to fourteen.

Alban Woodroffe had moved on and was now chairman of the Dorset County Council Education Committee. And he had managed to get Lyme Regis its own grammar school. Until a permanent school could be built, it would be housed in some former army huts he had found on Salisbury Plain, on a site on the aptly named Hill Road.

The new grammar school in its temporary army buildings in Hill Road, looking eastwards over the town.

The school represented a victory for Alban over the Board of Education, who had claimed that the town had too few pupils to justify a grammar school. It was said that he visited every house in Lyme where there was a child eligible to take the entrance exam, often arriving in his chauffeur-driven car, and personally invigilated the exam behind locked doors. Every child passed, creating a national record. At first he had envisaged a school for boys only but, because of the need to swell numbers, it included girls from the start.

The new school would not be free. 'I went there because my father could pay', explained one former pupil. But in July 1923 the council agreed to offer two borough scholarships: one for a boy and one for a girl, each with an annual value of £12 15s.0d for five years to cover the fees and cost of books. The scholarship exam, open to all resident children not over twelve years six months on 1st September, would take place in September.

Winter storms pounded the Marine Parade and Alderman Wiscombe, whose building firm A.& F.Wiscombe was putting up the *Bay Hotel*, agreed to pay the council 11s. a cart load for any shingle and sand washed up onto the roadway for use in the building.

The *Bay Hotel* on the Marine Parade

1924 began with Big Ben's chimes being broadcast by the BBC for the first time, and at the end of January King George V asking Ramsay MacDonald to form the first Labour government. It survived until October.

Early February that year was unusually warm. The *Bridport News* reported that an adder measuring 2ft. 3 ins. (68 cms) long had been killed by Mrs Frost near the Charmouth Road, and two young ladies had been noticed bathing on the sea-front. In Bridport C.E.Bazley's was advertising a Triumph Motorcycle Combination Deluxe for £110: well over a year's wages for a working man.

To serious matters. For whatever reason – quite possibly in protest at the unreliability of her electricity supply – Mrs Sole had not paid her bill and owed the council £3 9s.0d. It cut her off. And the Borough's budget for the year beginning April 1924 estimated that the town's public lighting would cost £400 compared with £350 for feeding and stabling the corporation horses, but that receipts from electricity consumers should bring in £994.

Another source of council income was the harbour at the Cobb. Mooring charges were weighted heavily in favour of locals at the expense of visitors. For boats over 14 feet (4.3m) in length it charged sailors 1s.6d a day or 5s. a week, but only 15s. for the year.

In March 1924 Engineer Weekes put out to tender his detailed 'General Stipulations and Conditions for the Supply, Delivery and Erection of Additional Power Plant, Overhead Mains Etc at Lyme Regis, Dorset'. As well as the new DC generating plant, there would need to be new boosters and balancers, switches and dials, feeders and street lights, and underground and overhead mains cabling throughout the town.

Fourteen companies submitted quotes, ranging from £6,629 2s.10d to £9,054 9s.1d. The council chose the cheapest, G.E.Taylor & Co, and at the same time asked Weekes if he would mind reducing his fee. He politely declined. Taylor's quote included £1,128 for the new 50kW generator, £922 for the 264 accumulators for the battery house, £779 for a new switchboard and £2,920 for the town's new mains and street lighting. Of Lyme's 103 street lamps, only those down the hill through Broad Street and others along the Marine Parade would have 100-watt bulbs. The rest were to be '30-watt 220 volt metal filament lamps'. Not much threat to the grandeur of the star-filled night sky from them.

Taylor & Co also had to remove the redundant equipment, which was then offered for sale. A 'Gardner Horizontal Paraffin Engine, Size 8' was offered for £25; a 'Morris Hawkins Dynamo, Belt-driven' for £7 10s.0d, and a 'Gilkes Single Discharge Horizontal Shaft Water Turbine' for £5.

By the end of the month the Bridport News reported that 'Workman are busily engaged building the new accumulator room [battery house] at the Electric Light Works. Residents are keenly looking forward to the day when they will be able to have a supply of electricity throughout the whole day instead of having to go without for several hours, and just at the time when many of them require it.'

However, in June Mrs Sole still hadn't paid her £3 9s.0d electricity bill and was informed the council was going to take her to court. It was obviously getting nervous about the looming costs of the changeover from 110 volts to the new 440-volt system, and notified Mr Raymond that the discount it allowed him for electricity in the Assembly Rooms cinema would have to be discontinued from his September meter reading.

For the changeover, the council would have to bear the cost of replacing every light bulb in the town and replace or adapt almost every other piece of electrical equipment. It therefore distributed 200 notices to its existing consumers explaining the voltage change. However, light bulbs were expensive so, in order to minimise its bill for replacements, the council put a freeze on accepting new consumers until after the changeover. They could pay for their own bulbs then. Applicants for connection joined a waiting-list from which applications would eventually be considered one by one by the Electricity Committee, presumably to ensure that electricity was extended only to the right sort of household.

Elsewhere in the town in that summer of 1924, the Eddison Steam Rolling Co busied itself in the streets with its ten-ton roller for £1 17s.0d a day including driver, water-cart and fuel, and in the Langmoor Gardens the caretaker was instructed to prohibit the playing of games. In September Surveyor McDonnell reported that the chairs bought for the Gardens in July for £17 18s.6d had already brought in £34 11s.6d, and that after paying the chair-attendant his 5 per cent commission.

Down at the Cobb, however, there were complaints about the behaviour of 'certain boatmen licensed to ply for hire'. Council minutes record that 'terrible language was used by one man when another boatman "robbed" him of his freight. Touting for hire, although prohibited, is still going on.' The council threatened not to renew offending boatmen's licences.

Preparing for the voltage changeover was putting great pressure on Engineer Arthur Brown and his Electricity Department. At the end of the summer the council instructed him 'to endeavour to secure the services of a suitable office boy', and in the autumn the minutes record, 'It having been reported that Mr Brown, the resident engineer, had to devote 90 hours a week to his work, it was decided to advertise for a third assistant, and that C.Camplin's wages be raised from 25s. to 30s. per week.' For just 73 weeks' wages, a new Triumph Motorcycle Combination Deluxe could now be his.

The council also resolved that 'Mr Brown's residence at 5a Coombe Street be redecorated at a cost of £25 15s.0d'. In the run-up to the changeover it was keen to keep Arthur happy, and clearly that entailed keeping Mrs Brown happy too. And to attract as many new consumers as possible to connect when the changeover was complete, it offered to pay the cost of laying the first fifteen yards of underground cable to their houses from the road.

However, council generosity had its limits. Paul & Son's application for a lower electricity price for 'trade purposes' was rejected, as was Mr Robinson's for permission to place a 'penny-in-the-slot chocolate machine' in Broad Street.

By the end of 1924 there were 44 new consumers on the waiting-list to be connected to electricity, including four householders just across the Devon border in Uplyme. And the council had accepted a tender of £243 18s.10d from the Stella Lamp Co Ltd to supply all the replacement light bulbs it needed for the town.

Broad Street looking down towards the Assembly Rooms. Note the early street lamp. Central white lines to guide motorists were not introduced in England until 1927.

NEW GENERATION

The exact date when the new 440-volt generating equipment in the Malthouse thundered into life is not recorded. It seems to have been on or about New Year's Day 1925. Certainly by early February a Mr Rees had presented the council with a petition signed by forty residents 'living in the vicinity of the power station complaining about the noise and vibration caused by the new generating engine'. In Dorset, for forty people to get together, sign a petition, deliver it to the local council and have it discussed would probably have taken a good month, providing they were really, really cross.

The villain of the peace will have been the new 50kW dynamo driven by its 80HP Marshall diesel engine. The council seems to have taken no immediate action but at the end of the year Engineer Weekes advised that to reduce the noise, they needed to make alterations to the engine's new silencing pit. This was a large underground concrete chamber through which exhaust smoke and gases swirled before being piped up out through the roof. Whether the alterations made any difference is doubtful. Throughout its life, various attempts made to reduce the Malthouse noise and vibration had little if any effect.

The 50kW Marshall with its exhaust pipe on the left leading down to the silencing pit below.

Otherwise, the changeover appears to have proceeded smoothly. There must have been a few days when consumers had to resort to candles and oil or gas lamps while the new machinery and mains were being connected and their light bulbs replaced. However, given the unreliability of the old 110-volt supply, anyone with electric lights in Lyme Regis at that time would have had alternative means of lighting readily to hand.

For only a handful of consumers will the changeover have caused serious inconvenience. These were the people who had already begun to use electricity for heating and cooking. Council minutes in March recorded 'the redistribution of the heating and cooking apparatus after re-wiring to suit the new voltage has only recently been effected'. For just a couple of winter months these householders – or rather their servants – will have had to return to their open fires and the old kitchen range.

As well as the expense of new light bulbs and rewired 'apparatus' in private homes, the council had to buy the Star Tea Company a replacement coffee grinder for £12 10s.0d and pay £31 7s.0d to have the motors on Mr Geake the dentist's drills re-wound. But it watched the pennies carefully. Mr Haddon, who owned a drapers shop up Broad Street and supplied the Bathing Committee with costumes for rent to summer visitors, put in a claim in May for £1 14s.6d for bulbs he alleged had burst in January as a result of 'a surge in voltage'. The Electricity Committee rejected the claim because of his delay in making it. He tried again in June. This time the Committee put his claim to the vote: it lost by three votes to two.

Now faced with servicing the £13,000 loan borrowed to pay for the changeover, the council was nervous. It needed new customers and also to persuade existing consumers to start using more electricity for cooking and heating. It now had a two-price tariff: a lighting-rate at a shilling a unit, and a power-rate at fourpence. To take advantage of the power-rate, consumers needed to have a separate power circuit wired into their homes and to pay for a separate meter. Nevertheless, the proposition was attractive, especially as the price of electrical goods in the shops was falling.

Electricity sales started to rise. Although in the first quarter of 1925 most cookers and heaters in town were out of action being rewired, new consumers from the waiting-list were connected and sales of current were up nearly 40 per cent to £965, compared with £699 a year ago. Even more demand was on the horizon: as well as new homes and a hotel, existing consumers in Lyme were using more and there were applications for connection from people across the county boundary in Uplyme. Axminster Rural District Council gave Lyme Regis the necessary consent to supply.

This surge in demand was not what Consultant Engineer Weekes or anyone else had foreseen when he drew up his original modernisation scheme back in 1921. Just three months after the changeover, he wrote warning that by next winter the town's 70kW generating capacity would be practically fully loaded. The solution he proposed was to replace the old Gardner with its new 20kW dynamo with a new 100kW generating set.

The Electricity Department considered its figures. From when it bought the undertaking in July 1923 to the end of March 1924, revenue was £1,917. After generating costs of just over £460 including fuel and wages, Arthur Brown's salary of £145 10s.0d a year and a few other costs, the undertaking had still made a surplus of £1,150 14s.8d. Figures for 1924-25 were not yet available but all the signs were encouraging.

That spring the council asked the Electricity Commissioners to approve a further loan to buy not the single 100kW generator Weekes originally recommended but two 75kW sets. Two generators would provide more security of supply than one, and with the 50kW Marshall installed in January they would bring the Malthouse total generating capacity up to 200kWs, far more than they would ever need in the foreseeable future. At its June meeting the council agreed to buy the two new generators and also authorised Borough Electrical Engineer Brown to buy two dozen light bulbs.

The General Electric Company Ltd and Vickers-Petters Ltd were among nine companies who tendered for the new equipment. GEC won with a quote of £2,930. The managing director of Vickers-Petters, however, believed that Mr Weekes had handled the tendering process unethically, a belief he held strongly enough to send his London manager, Mr Bacon, down to Lyme Regis to complain to the council personally. Mr Bacon will probably have travelled down by rail: '3 1/2 hours from Waterloo by Express Train' proclaimed the town's advertisements; that and the little engine which puffed up the final winding branch from Axminster, where you left the Exeter Express.

Mr Bacon presented Vickers-Petters' case. Apparently this fellow Weekes had told GEC that if they reduced their original quote by a further £100 they would produce a winning bid. They had, in effect, been allowed to bid twice. And that, not to put too fine a point on it, was jolly unfair.

Mayor Bragg then asked Weekes for his side of the story. He explained that GEC was the only bidder whose equipment included diesel engines manufactured by Marshall & Son. As the Electricity Department already had one Marshall – the new 50kW set – then if the price were right he favoured sticking with the same manufacturer. What he had done made technical sense and also saved the council money. The council thanked Mr Bacon for his trouble and confirmed the contract with GEC.

In October builder William Caddy began work on the foundations for the first of the two new 75kW engines, and Arthur Brown put in a claim for £5 10s.6d travelling expenses to Gainsborough in Lincolnshire. His trip can only have been to visit Marshall Sons & Co whose works was there.

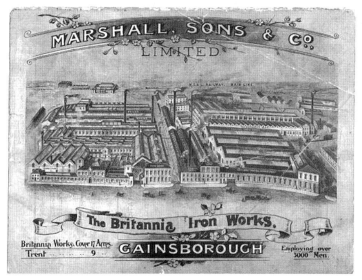

The Marshall works in about 1900, 'Employing over 3,000 Men'

In December 1925 Weekes wrote to the Electricity Committee. 'I have pleasure in reporting that the first of the 75kW engines was put on load on Friday 6th November and successfully supplied the whole town'. He went on to say that because the engine was smokier than expected they had added five feet (1.5m) to the exhaust chimney. The redundant 20kW generator was being removed to make room for Mr Caddy to start laying the foundations for the second Marshall with its GEC dynamo, which were due to arrive in the next few days together with a supply of spare parts.

There was just one last point, he said. The new engines would need servicing, which would involve periodically removing their pistons. These were so large, however, that the only safe way to extract them would be to use lifting-tackle suspended from an overhead runway.

Herbert Morris & Co would install a suitable system for £66 19s.0d. Should he go ahead and order it? And just one other final last point. The ceiling above the engines was made of matchboard, a significant fire risk. Could it be replaced with an asbestos ceiling? William Caddy could put one up for just £11 15s.0d. Thank you Mr Weekes. Anything. Just do it.

The changeover had been a success. In December, although the debit balance in its capital account had now risen to £16,955 5s.6d, the Electricity Department's revenue account was £1,094 5s.6 in credit and the council awarded pay rises. Arthur Brown got £26 more a year, and Assistant Engineers Curtis and Mills 5s. and Camplin 10s. more a week. However, the rise was not enough for First Assistant Curtis and he handed in his notice. The council received 32 applications for his post.

Elsewhere in the town modernisation pushed forward apace. The first woman councillor had been elected. In February 1925 the council considered a request to provide its outdoor workmen with 'oilskin suits as they have to be out in all winds and weather', and also to grant them a week's annual holiday*. And in June it reversed its earlier decision to purchase a new horse and cart for watering the streets, and instead bought its first motor lorry.

The new lorry made by a Birmingham firm called Garner cost £600. It was fitted with a 450-gallon water tank and solid rubber tyres. The council ordered it to be painted 'a light drab and lettered Corporation of Lyme Regis'. A shed was prepared in Pooles Court between the national school and gasworks to keep it safe and dry, and a notice advertising for a motor-mechanic/driver was posted on the Guildhall door. Mr Perry got the job at £2 5s.0d a week.

A Garner lorry of the late 1920s.

Down on the River Lym, Oswald Fowler of the Town Mill finally got round to repairing the 'hatches' by the Silk Mill for flushing the river. It seems the Mill had rights and duties over the river even above the weir at Gosling Bridge that fed its mill-leat. Flushing the river was the age-old way of cleansing the riverbed of all the filth and rubbish that found its way in. The process consisted of building up a head of water behind wooden hatches and then, to the delight of children of all ages, releasing it so that a wall of water swept all the debris down the river and into the sea. Apparently the smell it stirred up was awful.

In July, John Raymond of the Assembly Rooms Cinema and Tea-rooms, applied to carry out alterations to the lobby so that an attendant could sell 'summer drinks and sweets and ices'. This would, he explained, allow Mrs Raymond to close her tearooms on Sundays.

Not all in town was sweetness and light. On the seafront a boatman, 'who was the worse for drink', capsized his rowing boat with two passengers aboard, throwing them into the sea,

* The council, possibly stunned by the scale of these requests, passed them on for consideration by the Highways Committee.

and had his licence suspended. There were also reports of 'unruly children' in the Langmoor Gardens. In the autumn the *Royal Lion* in Broad Street was refusing to pay its electricity bill because it claimed the voltage changeover in January had burned out the element of its grill. And the new Catholic priest was refusing to pay his predecessor's share of the presbytery's bill despite the latter's claim that this was 'traditional'.

But the vicar's application to have the Parish Church of St Michael's connected for electric light was granted, and at the end of the year the council agreed to invest £21 in 'an instrument for locating faults in underground cables without the need to dig up considerable distances of road'.

In the mid-1920s there were literally hundreds of private and council-owned electricity companies in England, producing a bewildering variety of voltages and frequencies in direct or alternating currents. In London, for instance, there was such a patchwork of suppliers that there was no certainty you could take a light bulb from one side of a street and screw it into a house on the other without risk of it exploding.

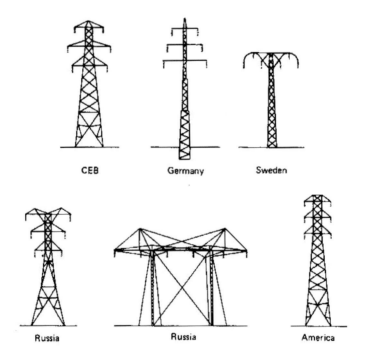

In 1926, Parliament passed the Electricity Supply Act. This gave the Government the powers it needed to set up a national grid. The grid would require all the main generating stations to standardise their voltages and adopt a common frequency (50 hertz) so it could be transmitted around the country. The aim was to reduce prices, with a target of 1d per unit by 1940, and also to produce a reliable national electricity supply for modern industry.

There was lots of opposition. The Conservatives opposed the grid because it involved the state meddling in perfectly good private enterprise. The electricity companies feared the grid would cost them local independence, control and very possibly jobs. And country-lovers feared the visual impact that the transmission lines, strung between bare steel towers across the countryside, would have on England's green and pleasant land.

To appease this last group, the distinguished architect Sir Reginald Blomfield RA was commissioned to help design the towers. He favoured the American style to cheaper European designs, and further softened it by diverging from the parallel at the second, rather than third, level. The towers soon became known as pylons. A pylon was 'the monumental gateway to an Egyptian temple', a popular association for a public recently enthralled by the discovery of Tutankhamen's tomb.

However, it would be 1928 before the construction of the national grid began, and another twenty before it reached Lyme Regis. For the time being, the town would continue with its own 440-volt three-wire DC system.

One great advantage of DC (direct current) electricity is that, unlike AC (alternating current), you can store it in batteries for use later. This allowed the generating station, with its associated manpower costs and, in Lyme Regis, noise to be closed down while still keeping the system alive. However a major disadvantage of DC is that it can only be distributed over a distance of two or three miles without an excessive voltage drop, so although it is fine for villages and small towns, DC is totally unsuited to large cities. A second major disadvantage is that it is difficult to transform the voltage of DC.

With AC on the other hand, although it cannot be stored like DC, you can easily change its voltage with a transformer. It is this ability to transform voltage that enables current to be transmitted very efficiently at high voltage over great distances with little loss of power. Through the national grid, electricity was transmitted around the country at a standard 132,000 volts (132kV). At its destination, the high voltage was transformed down in steps through substations, eventually to the 240 volts required by domestic consumers, or other voltages that industrial users might require.

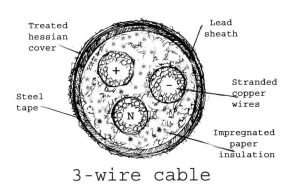

3-wire cable

Lyme Regis, however, did not have AC, but its 3-wire DC system offered a clever way to provide industrial users with a higher voltage than ordinary household electricity. Of the three wires, one was positive, one negative and the third neutral. (I am assured this was achieved by two rotary balancers connected between the outers, and a common bond which was called the neutral, so there you are.)

But what it boiled down to in practical terms was that the 440 volts were split into 220 volts in the positive wire and 220 volts in the negative. Mrs Smith's house was connected to the positive and neutral, Mrs Robinson next door to the negative and neutral, and so on alternating house by house down the street. Their lights and other equipment therefore operated on 220 volts. However, when the cable reached Mr Bun the Baker with his heavy-duty dough-mixing machine, the fitters ignored the neutral wire and connected him to the positive and negatives, thus delivering 440 volts: the potential difference between the two live wires.

Despite the two-part tariff with the lower rate of 4d a unit for power, electricity was still a good deal more expensive in Lyme Regis than in other parts of the country. One workshop owner complained he had paid £90 11s.4d over the previous 12 months for power and it was 'impossible to carry on a business such as mine at these prices'. Other consumers suspected the accuracy of their electricity meters. Eventually, Arthur Brown tested a sample of ten. The apparently satisfactory result he reported was that eight of the meters were correct or in the consumer's favour, while only two were in the council's.

1926 began with a motorist's insurers denying liability for the £9 13s.6d damage done to a lamp standard in Broad Street by their client's motor car (but offering half that amount in settlement). The Electricity Department agreed to pay half the cost of a new element for the grill at the *Royal Lion* which the hotel claimed had been damaged in the voltage changeover. And for the Malthouse, Arthur Brown was empowered to 'procure a good white distemper for the woodwork and to have the stonework limewashed'.

The 1926 edition of *Garckes Manual* estimated that, with all the new customers on the waiting-list now connected up, the total number of domestic and business electricity consumers in the town had reached three hundred.

HARD TIMES

For most people, the mid-1920s were hard. In Lyme Regis, at the Armistice Day service in November 1924, the vicar reminded the congregation that although much had been done for war widows and orphans, 'the poor crippled men who cannot now find work are neglected'.

By 1925 unemployment was a national problem. From below 5 per cent in 1920 it had soared and remained at well over 10 per cent through the 1920s. It peaked in 1932 at 22.1 per cent. As for the general economy, in 1926 the GDP per capita was less than it had been in 1906.

One victim of unemployment was Harry Lewis, a blacksmith of no fixed abode, who in January 1926 appeared before Mayor Bragg at the Guildhall police court accused of attempted burglary. Mrs Emily Pitcher of 33 Coombe Street had been woken at about 2.00am by the sound of breaking glass. The sound apparently came from the Bridport Co-op, the shop next door. She had called out, 'Who's there?' There was a mumbled response so she had sent Mr Pitcher off to wake up Sergeant Carter at the police station in Coombe Street.

At about 4.00am after a search, Sergeant Carter found Lewis asleep in a railway carriage in a siding up at the station and arrested him. At first Lewis denied any knowledge of glass breaking in Coombe Street or anywhere else, but some close questioning by the sergeant eventually produced a full confession.

Mayor James Bragg

Lewis told the court, 'I plead guilty to the charge. The reason I done it was because I was out of work and on the verge of starvation. I have walked a hundred miles in search of work and I have failed.' He added (in suspiciously good grammar), 'I would like to thank the Sergeant for the generous treatment he has accorded me whilst under arrest.' The *Bridport News* concluded, 'The Mayor said the bench would commit the accused for trial and wished to commend the police for the smart manner in which the arrest was affected.'

For homeless drifters like Harry Lewis there was still, if they were desperate, the workhouse.

The Poor Law system that spawned them dated back to Elizabeth I and did not end until 1930. There was no workhouse in Lyme, but neighbouring Axminster, Beaminster and Bridport all had them. Across Dorset there were fifteen. In England and Wales you had a choice of 643.

Less than a year before Lewis's arrest, the Ministry of Health had sent an inspector called Duff to report on the workhouse in Bridport. He said the children looked happy and the chapel was 'very nice'. Mr Duff asked the Master what they did with the children, and the Master told him that they boarded them out 'as it took the children away from the Workhouse Taint'.

The *Bridport News* report continued, 'The number of inmates in the institution in the week ended February 14th was 70. These vagrants numbered 68 men and 2 women. The inspector asked the Master if he knew they were bound to provide tramps with a midday meal according to law.' Mr Jones must have indicated he did not because 'The inspector said that if a vagrant going along the street fell down and died and they brought in a verdict of death from starvation, "You would be the man they would hang"'. The Master told Mr Duff that the men got eight ounces (227 gms) of bread and ½ ounce of margarine for breakfast. However, 'The bread broke up but it was worthless, and some of the men cleaned their boots with the margarine.'

The old workhouse in Bridport, now converted into luxury flats.

Dr P.N.Cook had taken over from Dr Spurr as the borough's medical officer of health. His annual reports give unique insights into Lyme Regis. For 1924 he estimated the town's population at 2,311 and reported 37 legitimate and four illegitimate births, and 29 deaths. In 1925 there were 29 births (all legitimate) and 20 deaths; and in 1926, 25 legitimate and five illegitimate births and 32 deaths. These separate figures for legitimate and illegitimate births reflect the social attitudes of the day, as did a resolution the council considered in 1926: 'That medical officers in charge of maternity centres be allowed to give information on birth-control in certain cases'. The council could not decide. 1926 was the year it became legally possible for parents to make a child legitimate by marrying after it had been born.

Dr Cook compared Lyme's birth and death rates with the national averages over five years. In Lyme there were 15.8 births per 1,000 population compared with a national figure of 17.8, and deaths were 12.4 per 1,000 compared with 11.6 nationally. At first glance these figures might suggest that Lyme Regis was unhealthy. In fact they reflected older people choosing to retire to the town, and younger people choosing to leave and have their families elsewhere.

11 HARD TIMES

In his 1925 report Dr Cook stated there were 15 families receiving Poor Law Relief, largely in the form of free medical treatment, and that the cost of this relief to the borough was £178 19s.2d for the year. He noted that the Jubilee Cottage Hospital, founded in 1897 in Church Street, had seven beds, an operating theatre, an x-ray machine, and an outpatients department. There had been one case of TB in the town in 1924 and none in 1925, but nine in 1926. The nearest hospital for infectious diseases was in Bridport. Lyme had one certified midwife.

Dr Cook's report continued, 'There are three private slaughterhouses in the town, which are clean but badly situated, being too near dwelling houses', and the water supply was still unsatisfactory. 'During the summer months when there is a large influx of visitors, the water is cut off at certain periods of the day.' However water from a spring at Cathole Farm was to be piped to a new reservoir to be built near the railway station, and he was optimistic that this would solve the problem. (It did not.)

The town's milk supply, on the other hand, he described as 'excellent'. There were four dairies and a milk shop, which were inspected quarterly and kept in good order. The cows were free from disease, probably, he thought, because the mild climate allowed them to be kept outside throughout the year. There was no pasteurisation of milk in the area. Interestingly, the mother of one of the families in Corporation Terrace, who was diagnosed with TB, was prescribed a free pint of this unpasteurised milk per day as part of her treatment, on the orders of the County Medical Officer.

Workmen clearing earth from the Marine Parade near the Bay Hotel after the 1926 landslides.

The coastline around Lyme Regis, both east and west, is notoriously unstable. This instability may delight fossil hunters and is why developers have never managed to sprawl the town out along the coast, but landslides are frequent.

In February 1925 there was a minor slip in the town itself, which fellow councillors accused the mayor James Bragg of reporting badly to the press. An exaggerated article had appeared in the *Daily Mail* with the result, his colleagues claimed, that 'a number of people had come down expecting to find Lyme Regis in the sea'.

Other slips to the east had permanently closed the old coastal road to Charmouth below the golf course, except to those on horseback or on foot. Horse-drawn and motor traffic heading east to Bridport and Dorchester now had to clamber up Timber Hill to Penn Cross and then take the inland route to Charmouth. The road was cruelly steep, and the following autumn Alban Woodroffe gifted the land needed to build the present gentler stretch of road leading eastwards out of town.

At the start of 1926 there were some far more serious landslips in the Langmoor Gardens above the Marine Parade. According to the *Bridport News*, 'The gardens are so ruined and the destruction so complete that it will be impossible to reconstruct them. Gangs of men have been at work every day including Sunday and huge quantities of earth have been thrown into the sea.' The council erected two gantries on the Marine Parade to carry the debris down across the beach.

These new landslips again made the national papers. The Advertising Committee, whose job it was to promote the town to visitors, wrote to Mayor Bragg in despair. Local reporters had been deliberately angling their photographs to exaggerate the seriousness of the landslide, they complained. 'In a town which relies entirely on visitors for its existence, these reporters are doing their best to bring ruin to the Borough. It is high time their activities were checked.'

Whether Mayor Bragg could have checked the press even if he had wanted to is doubtful, but Mayoress Rosa Bragg did her bit to defend the town's tourist industry: she presented the museum with the blue shark caught off the coast the previous August which she had had stuffed. The council recorded its thanks.

These were hungry days and a year later 'to relieve the prevailing unemployment', the council instructed Surveyor Major McDonnell to arrange to have the last of the landslip earth removed from the Marine Parade and a new drainage system installed in the Langmoor Gardens in the vain hope that this would prevent it happening again. Local labour was to be used, 'preference to be given to married men'. No nonsense about equal opportunities in Lyme Regis those days, but the encouragement to get married may have worked: from five illegitimate births in 1926, the figure had fallen to one in 1929.

As for farm labourers, at a meeting of the Agricultural Wages Committee in Dorchester in May 1926, the committee rejected a proposal 'that the pay for male workers of 21 years of age and over be increased by three shillings to £1 13s. 0d per week of 51 hours in summer, and 48 hours in winter'. The farmers said they could not afford the rise and, anyway, as prices had generally fallen over the last few years, their farm labourers must in fact already be better off now than they had been a year or so ago.

They did not, however, go as far as the mine owners in coalfields across the country who demanded their miners accept longer hours for lower pay. They were having to compete with cheap imported coal from Germany which, in its turn, was trying to pay the punitive war reparations imposed on it at the end of the war.

Britain's coal industry then employed 1.2 million men. The miners resisted the employers' demands and, in May 1926, the rest of the trades union movement briefly supported them. The General Strike 'in defence of miners' wages and hours' lasted nine days but failed to bring the country to a standstill. On 12th May the TUC called it off and gradually life returned to normal. The miners held out through the summer but hardship slowly crushed them. By the autumn most had been driven resentful back to work.

Compared with Manchester which was brought to a halt and Sheffield where 50,000 men came out, the General Strike hardly touched Lyme Regis. The station was closed and there were no national newspapers, but the local press continued to appear. Coal rationing was introduced and the council's Emergency Committee appointed Mr E.J.Stoward as 'coal controller' at a salary of £1 15s.0d a week. If there had been any dockers down at the Cobb they might have struck, but there were none: the medical officer of health's reports for both 1925 and 1926 state 'no ships entered or left the port in the year'. However, Lyme's postmen seemed to have joined the strike as the postmistress asked the council for authority 'to allow persons willing to carry the mail to do so'. The only other reference to the strike in council minutes was in June: 'It was decided to continue without the public lighting', but this because of a national fuel shortage caused by the miners, not a strike at the Malthouse.

On Saturday 7th July 1926 there was a spectacular storm across the region. The *Bridport News* called it the worst thunderstorm on record. In delightfully dated prose it told readers, 'For nine hours the storm encircled the town in a manner which was appalling to even the stoutest heart'. Windows were broken by hailstones larger than marbles. Storm water drains in Broad Street were burst, ripping up huge slabs of pavement, and the *Royal Lion Hotel* and several houses on the street were flooded, with 'the rushing torrent of the river under Bridge Street carrying large branches of trees and garden produce. The flood waters down Broad Street converted the Square into a second river, and at daybreak more than one housewife could be seen in tears as she viewed the destruction that had been wrought.' Several horses were killed by the lightning and Mayor Bragg was astir at 3am seeing what could be done. His own grocery store in Coombe Street was flooded out.

Landslides and storms to one side, there was a constant threat to the town from fire. In the Civil War, when most of its houses were thatched, a large number were set on fire by the Royalists during the Siege of Lyme. Two hundred years later in 1844, fire burned down many of the closely packed medieval houses in and around Coombe Street, and people could still remember the last major blaze in 1889 which destroyed part of Broad Street.

Members of the fire brigade in the mid-1920s.

Herbert Foxwell ran a plumbing and glazing firm, had one of the first telephones in town (Lyme Regis 4), had been Borough Water Bailiff in charge of the municipal water supply for nearly forty years and, appropriately, also led the part-time Victoria Fire Brigade as its captain. Under his command were a lieutenant and twelve firemen, equipped with splendid polished brass helmets and a hand-drawn fire-engine. 'Persons of good character alone' were eligible to enter the brigade, and they were paid per fire and for twelve practice drills a year. Smoking was 'strictly prohibited at Fires and on Parade'.

11 HARD TIMES

In his annual report for 1926, Captain Foxwell told the council that during the year the brigade had attended six fires. Five had been quickly put out but one at Summerhill (the house where A.S.Neill ran his famous 'freedom school') had resulted in an estimated loss of £500. The annual cost of the fire brigade to the rate-payers was £62 17s.2d, including £40 14s.6d in payments to the men for attending fires and drills. The following year Neill moved his Summerhill School and its children away to the relative safety of Norfolk.

12
BESIDE THE SEASIDE

If you have had enough of electricity for a bit, this chapter is for you. It is all about Lyme as a seaside resort. It is social history: interesting and entirely non-electrical stuff.

At the start of my story, Lyme Regis had already been a seaside resort for over a hundred years. The arrival of the railway in 1903 opened it up to more visitors. However, in those days the cement works and commercial port were still alive, so it was not until the 1920s and '30s that tourism came to dominate the economy of the town.

Despite the Depression, most people in England were markedly better off at the end of the 1930s than they were at the end of the First World War. As well as better wages, more and more employees were securing the right to an annual holiday with pay. Visitor numbers in Lyme and other seaside towns grew steadily. From being just a dream, a week by the sea and even a motor car to get there in had become a real possibility for many ordinary families.

As well as spending money in local businesses, visitors to Lyme Regis contributed directly to the borough's finances. They paid for car parks and putting greens, deck chairs and public lavatories. And then there was why they came there in the first place: the sea.

Before the First World War, the council divided the main beach between Cobb Gate and the Cobb into five bathing sections and let them out at the start of every season by tender. The local person or family who won a particular section would then hire out changing tents, deck-chairs, towels and bathing costumes. They would also rent space for people to erect their own changing tents, but whether you hired a tent or put up your own, you had to have a tent. Changing without a tent was strictly forbidden, so one way or another, everyone had to pay to bathe.

73

In 1911 Mayor Woodroffe reported that the annual tendering for the five sections of beach 'had caused a little friction', so the system was changed. The whole beach was put out to tender as a single lot, with the person who won it allowed to sub-let sections. The winner also had to provide 'a man who could swim' as a lifeguard on the beach.

At the start of 1914 Mr and Mrs Toms won the beach for the season with a bid of £81. However, the outbreak of war caused visitor numbers to drop sharply so the council waived part of the first season's rent. In 1916, the Toms won the beach again, with a bid of only £61.

In 1917 the bids were so few and so low that the council decided to run the bathing business itself. It bought up the changing tents and deck-chairs from its former beach-tenants, and their stocks of towels and bathing caps and costumes. It also bought new ones from Mr Bosence the outfitter: '9 men's costumes @ 2s.6½d each and 3 outsize men's @ 2s.10d each'. For the 1917 season it ordered 7,000 fourpenny adult bathing tickets, 3,000 tuppenny (2d) junior tickets, 5,000 dress and towel tickets (2d), and 1,000 penny tickets for deck-chairs.

Tickets now had to be bought for each of four daily bathing sessions from a council ticket office on the Marine Parade. For serious swimmers there was a bracing first shift from 7am to 8.30am. Then came the main family sessions from 9.30am to 1pm and 2pm to 4.30pm. Finally there was the evening swim from 5.30pm to 7pm. Presumably the gap between sessions was to allow people to pack up and leave the beach or buy a ticket for the next shift.

If you were in Lyme for a week or two you could hire your own private tent from the Harbour Master for 7s.6d a week (10s. in August). This saved you the trouble of queuing for bathing tickets and gave you a permanent base on the beach. In response to reports that certain visitors were changing into their bathing costumes at their lodgings and then sneaking down to the beach in mackintoshes to swim without paying, the council passed a by-law that 'between the hours of 8am and 8pm no person shall use for the purpose of bathing any part of the sea-shore without a tent'.

Mr and Mrs Gratten, former beach-tenants, were appointed male and female bathing attendants at a combined weekly wage of £2 15s.0d. Mr Gratten was to provide a safety boat during the hours of bathing, and Mrs Gratten was made 'responsible for the washing and care of the bathing dresses, including the repair of the same'. Owners of private tents 'desirous of employing an attendant other than their own personal servant' had to employ Mr Gratten, who was permitted to charge them not more than 6d a week or 5s. for the season.

In 1923 the council formed a Bathing Committee to run the beach, which reported that receipts for the season from adult bathers amounted to £263 and from juveniles of £41. Rents from tents came to £295, chairs £137 and bathing dress and towels £25. After paying the attendants' wages plus a seven per cent commission on their takings, the council's net profit from bathers came to £458.

There was also an Advertising Committee to promote the town. In 1923 it distributed 1,567 copies of its *Sunny Lyme Regis* guide, 200 more than in 1922, and managed to persuaded the Southern Railway Company to feature a picture of Lyme on the cover of its new 'Winter Resorts' booklet.

By 1926 the Advertising Committee was spending £50 a year advertising with Southern Railways and posted off 2,000 *Sunny Lyme Regis* guides. To keep visitors entertained, it issued licences to 32 boatmen and 50 pleasure boats, and did a deal with the Peerless Weighing Machine Co. In return for permission to place a penny-in-the-slot weighing machine on the Marine Parade, the company paid the council 25 per cent of its taking. At the end of the summer, Surveyor Major McDonnell reported, '11,202 persons have used the weighing machine in the past season'.

An Old and Historic Municipal Borough. Ideal Health Resort for Summer and Winter. Invigorating Air. Pure Water. Good Sanitation. Unrivalled Sea Bathing, Boating and Fishing. Golf Links. Tennis Courts. Sunshine equal to that of any place on the South Coast

For Official Guide giving full information of town and district, send 3d. stamps to

J. H. SHARLEY, Hon. Sec., Advertising Committee.

LYME REGIS.

HOTEL ALEXANDRA
Favourite Winter Resort

Close to and overlooking delightful Bay.

The only Hotel in its own Grounds in this English Riviera.

Table d'Hote at Separate Table. Central Heating. Electric Light throughout. Facing Sea and South. Excellent Cuisine. Tariff on Application. Special Winter Terms.

Telegrams: Alexandra. Telephone: No. 10.

A. H. HINTON, Proprietor.

LYME REGIS—" Pitt "-House Private Hotel.

Stands in its own Lovely Grounds of Two Acres, with its own Tennis and Croquet Courts. Exquisite Coastal Scenery. Close to Sea. Garage. Separate Tables. Electric Light throughout. " Pitt "-House stands first for Ideal Holiday and Winter Resort. Strictly Moderate Terms. Illustrated Tariff on application to ALBERT WRIGHT, Proprietor.

Tel.: " Pitt, Lyme Regis." Phone 65.

LYME REGIS—St. Michael's Private Hotel.

Central position, close to Public Gardens and Sea. Every modern convenience. Well appointed. Special terms Letween Seasons. Separate Tables. A.A., M.U.

In Southern Railway's *Hints for Holidays* 1925/26, the Alexandra and the Pitt boast 'Electric Light throughout'.

Despite the General Strike and the storm and flood in July, the 1926 season turned out well for the town. In August, the *Bridport News* reported that the Bathing Committee applauded when Councillor Camplin announced, 'The past week has been a record in the matter of bathing receipts, the parking of cars has been a financial success and everything is in a flourishing condition'.

However, not all visitors were happy to have to pay to swim. Charles Low from Middlesex wrote the following year to say that after his second visit to 'charming Lyme Regis', his only two criticisms were the lack of good tennis courts and 'the decidedly objectionable impost of 6d for the right to bathe within the ordinary limits of the foreshore'. Obviously not all other resorts charged people to swim.

Back at the start of 1926, there was a story in the *Bridport News* of a 'Runaway Char-a-banc' from Exeter. This had been making its way up Broad Street when it stalled and started to run backwards. The driver managed to steer it into the side of the road, crashing into the premises of Mr Geake the dentist. 'The back axle was broken, one wheel fell off, but the occupants escaped with a shaking.'

Motor cars were now becoming commonplace and the town was having to provide them with petrol and parking. Petrol pumps (hand-pumped) were appearing – until the First World War, motorists normally bought petrol by the can – and in 1926 the council gave Mr Baker permission to install one with a swinging arm at his garage opposite the Assembly Rooms. At the same meeting it granted Councillor the Reverend G.F.Eyre a licence to store 250 gallons (1,130 litres) of 'motor spirit' in an underground tank at his garage in Silver Street.

The Rev. G.F.Eyre's garage full of petrol. His chauffeur Mr Jarvis lived in the cottage
on the left while Lyme's postmaster, Mr Loosemore, rented the cottage on the right.

The council had not yet introduced parking charges at its small car-park at Cobb Gate beside the Assembly Rooms, but was just about to. In April a visitor from Shepton Mallet wrote complaining about 'loafers hanging around in the car park while posing as guardians. The owners [of cars] give more as a peace offering than for any service rendered.' The council's response was to advertise the post of parking attendant. As with its deck-chair attendants, he would be paid with a percentage of his takings.

The hills down into Lyme Regis are steep. Before the War, A. & F. Wiscombe ('Architectural Builders, Coach Builders, House Painters, Decorators and Undertakers') had advertised their Cosy Car for £15, 'fitted with Brake to suit the district.'

OUR COSY CAR, £15.

The trouble by the mid-1920s was that many visiting drivers and vehicles had neither the brakes nor the experience to suit the district, and there were a number of accidents. As well as the run-away charabanc and motorists crashing into lampposts, the brakes on one of W.H.Pinney & Co's coal lorries failed at the top of the town in Silver Street. A lady pedestrian only escaped with her life by smartly flattening herself into a doorway. To stop his lorry, the driver crashed it into a wall.

In response to this new danger, the council decided to erect five warning signs at the tops of the hills leading down to the town. These gave the length of the hill and counselled motorists in red lettering, 'Steady! Be Wise! Change Down!'

The estimate for the 1926 general district rates included £300 for street lighting, £200 for horses and stables and £125 for the corporation's new lorry. However, although they probably didn't know it, the days of council horses were now numbered.

The cottage hospital in Church Street was now considered too old and small. Councillor the Rev. G.F.Eyre lived in a large house above the town called Westhill. In its grounds his mother lived, in a house called Hernlea on Pound Road, with wonderful views over Lyme Bay to Portland Bill. After her death in the spring of 1926 the Reverend Eyre made a gift of Hernlea to the town as home for a new cottage hospital. It would have beds for five male and five female patients upstairs, and an operating theatre and accommodation for a matron and nurses on the ground floor. A fund was opened for donations for extra medical equipment and two presumably spinster sisters, named as the Misses Lister, donated £100.

The Reverend G.F.Eyre, Mayor 1926 - 1928 and 1935 - 1937

Lyme Regis may have looked after its sick in some style, but it had no time for yobbery. In June 1926, Norman Chalet and his wife Rosina were arrested for being drunk and disorderly in Church Street, shouting abuse at passers-by. The court was told that on his arrest, Chalet's excuse had been, 'Too much cider, Sergeant'. This failed to impress and the mayor sentenced the couple to 14 days' imprisonment.

Similarly when, at the end of that year, 14-year-old William Humphrey was brought before the bench for using indecent language in the street, the mayor fined him five shillings – a week's wages for an apprentice. The *Bridport News* reported that Superintendent Beck had told the court he was 'bringing the case forward as a warning to the defendant and other lads against whom numerous complaints had been made about their language'. 'Mayor Eyre warned Humphrey that much heavier penalties would be inflicted if he or others were brought before the court again and urged the police to continue their vigilance.'

A brief entry in council minutes in September 1926 hints that one of the key characters in bringing electricity to Lyme Regis had fallen on hard times. Councillors agreed not to take legal action against Mr T.G.Hains for the recovery of the amount due on his electricity account. Instead they accepted his offer to pay off the debt at five shillings a month for the next two months and ten shillings a month thereafter. This can only have been the same Mr T.G.Hains who, as 'bicycle and motor engineer of Bridge Street', had in 1908 persuaded Engineer Balbiani to come to the town, talked Alban Woodroffe into becoming chairman of the Electric Light Co and, according to *Pulmans Weekly*, 'must be looked upon as the pioneer of the electric light scheme'.

Things were not going too well either for Oswald Fowler, the last miller at the Town Mill. In autumn 1926, shortly before the Mill finally ground to a halt, he and his stepfather William Pinney appeared before the Lyme bench, charged with 'having for use for trade a weighing machine that was unjust'. The charge related to a coal-weighing machine at W.H.Pinney & Co's yard in Axminster.

The pair pleaded not guilty on the grounds that an employee had weighed the coal and they were not responsible for the acts of an employee. It emerged that the bar of the weighing machine had broken and been repaired by the employee, who had tied it up with string. However, Superintendent Beck told the court, Pinney & Co had been fined before for 'selling coal short', so the bench took a stern view and fined Oswald and William a fiver.

The autumn also saw the end of the old way of making up the borough's roads with crushed limestone and granite. In September council minutes record, 'The roads have been recently tarred for the first time, but some sections are so slippery as to be practically impassable by horses. Some grit has been laid pending re-tarring.' By the following May the council decided it was no longer worth the expense of watering the streets as they had all been tarred.

The town steamroller in 1911. The same machine was still in use in the early 1930s.

After its service as a hospital during the war, Alban Woodroffe had converted his house at Rhode Hill back into a private residence and moved there from Ware House in 1919. In October 1926 the *Bridport News* reported, 'The inhabitants of Uplyme and the surrounding districts were awakened by the sound of the parish bells, the occasion being the twenty-first birthday of the only son of the squire'.

It continued, 'The festivities were reminiscent of bygone days. They commenced with a ball on Wednesday night, and on Thursday, Mr Reginald Woodroffe's birthday, there was another ball for the employees, tenants and other friends connected with the Ware and Rhode Hill estates. A hundred or more guests were present.

'At supper Mr Tabberer, on behalf of the staff, expressed their good wishes and asked "Mr Rex" to accept a handsome clock, which was handed to him by Mrs Muller, who has been in the service of the family for more than forty-two years.' There were more gifts and on Friday a supper was given for the bell ringers. 'On Saturday Mr and Mrs Woodroffe kindly gave tea to the school children of Uplyme and the Boy Scouts. An excellent entertainment was given by Mr Maurice Charles, the well-known entertainer from London.'

Following more landslips to the east of the town, a permanent barrier was erected that autumn across the old coast road to Charmouth. Traffic had been struggling up the alternative inland route over Timber Hill, but now a new section of road on a gentler slope which by-passed the Hill was planned. In November 1926 under the heading 'Mr Woodroffe's Generous Gift', the *Bridport News* told readers that Alban 'had kindly agreed to give all the necessary land for the purpose of the road'.

The 22nd December edition of the paper carried news that William Thomas of Uplyme had been fined five shillings for having no front light on his motor lorry, and that Major F.H.McDonnell, recently retired Borough Surveyor, had entertained employees of the Town Council for dinner at *The Three Cups Hotel*. 'The company partook of a sumptuous spread and twice during the evening the guests insisted on singing, "For he's a jolly good fellow"'.

Major McDonnell had been ill for some time and had finally retired after two months' paid sick-leave. After consulting Axminster, Bridport and Wimbourne, the council agreed to pay the removal expenses of £28 for a new borough surveyor, Mr Ernest Prescott. As for Major McDonnell, the January minutes record under a heading 'The Late Surveyor' that £16 3s.1d of his salary was still owed. What with all the encouraging singing at *The Three Cups*, the signs were that he had shuffled off to join the choir celestial. I was therefore delighted to find him pop up again more than a decade later in council minutes: in May 1938, Major McDonnell accepted an offer of £2 10s.0d a week from the council to act as Part-time Assistant Surveyor.

HOMES FOR HEROES

In the mid-1920s, a shortage of decent housing was a problem throughout the country. In Lyme Regis, the medical officer of health Dr Cook was blunt in his report for 1924. 'Further accommodation is urgently required for the working classes'. He had inspected 40 houses during the year: 'one was unfit and seven more not in all respects fit for human habitation'.

Dr Cook estimated there were now about 450 inhabited houses in the town. 320 of these he described as 'cottages' – his term for working-class homes – and many of them were 'very old and too closely spaced'. About 300 had access to flushing water closets, often outdoors in yards or gardens nearby. The rest made do with earth closets or cesspits.

Lyme's first woman councillor, Mrs Bradford, was elected in November 1924. After their first meeting, the new council moved from the Guildhall to the museum next door for refreshments at 'the big table'. Following loyal toasts the oldest member, Councillor Camplin, congratulated fellow members on the fact that there were 20 council houses in the town whereas when he had joined the council there had been none. But then Mrs Bradford spoke up. She had recently 'been into a house in Broad Street and it was deplorable what the occupier had to live in. The landlords should be made at least to put the roofs in order to keep out the wet.'

The council was, however, now building eight new houses in Corporation Terrace, the first social housing since the war. They would be ready for occupation in the summer of 1926. Dr Cook noted, 'These will be similar to existing, but with bathroom accommodation, and will make it possible to condemn the most unsatisfactory housing in the town'.

The 20 original pre-war council houses. The eight new ones added in 1926 were almost identical but had bathrooms. In 1974 West Dorset District Council, in a fit of poshification, changed the name from Corporation Terrace to 'Lym Close'.

A stone plaque records that Corporation Terrace was begun in Alban Woodroffe's first mayoralty in 1911. It was built near the gas works with open fields behind and, apart from the almshouses, was the first public housing in Lyme. The pre-war scheme consisted of 20 houses in five short terraces, including the one the council had offered the Stoodleys in 1923 in its failed attempt to get them out of number 5 Coombe Street. Each house comprised a sitting room, kitchen, scullery and larder on the ground floor, three bedrooms upstairs and a small garden.

The building cost in 1911 worked out at £178 per house. The eight new houses with their added bathrooms would cost £487 each: £3,900 the lot. The council borrowed the money from the Public Works Loan Commission at 4¾ per cent and awarded the contract to local builder Charlie Hallett. Another reason for building council houses was to create local jobs.

After discussions in June 1927, the Housing Committee decided not to wire Corporation Terrace for electricity – they probably thought it would be far too expensive for council house tenants – but they did give the Devon Gas Association, which had taken over Mr Wallis's Gas & Range Co, permission to supply the houses with gas. At the same time they agreed to repair the coppers* and ranges in the twenty older houses at a cost of £46 10s.0d.

Lilly Collier, who grew up in Corporation Terrace, remembers her house being connected to electricity but much later, when she was 14 in 1937. 'Before the advent of electricity we only had paraffin lamps and candles. I also remember a gas lamp which was operated by chains to go on and off. All cooking was made on a coal range, which gave heating to our living room.' There were nine children in Collier family. 'We used to sleep head-to-toe,' she remembers. 'Ours was an older house so we didn't have a bathroom. I always wondered why some houses had bathrooms and others didn't. We had a tin bath.'

The Stoodleys had not wanted the council house they were offered in Corporation Terrace, but many people did. The eight new homes were seen as 'very clean, comfortable houses' and there was hot competition to get one.

At the end of April 1926, just before the houses were ready, the council received a letter from the Toms family. They had not been allocated one and wrote in the hope that the council would reconsider.

I have been married for four years. For over 12 months we lived with my parents, sharing a bedroom with his brothers, only parted off with a screen. We then moved to Uplyme, with a bedroom and use of a kitchen, for two years. This became overcrowded with a baby of nine months so we came back to Lyme to live in an attic with no fireplace for over 12 months until a person, knowing of our condition, offered to give us a room until we succeeded in finding a house.

Trusting you will compare our circumstances with those selected as tenants and reconsider the matter.

Yours faithfully,
S Toms

---

* A large vessel, formerly of copper, used for boiling or washing.

The next council meeting set the rent for the new houses at 11s. a week, and then voted on an amendment that S.Toms be selected as a prospective tenant in place of R.Camplin. The amendment was defeated. Not deterred Councillor Stock, seconded by the Reverend G.F.Eyre, then proposed S.Toms in place of Mrs H.Camplin. This proposal got five votes for and five against so Mayor Bragg was forced to use his casting vote. He cast it in favour of the Toms. The news must have been a blow to Mrs Camplin, but when in December Mr Bennett of 20 Corporation Terrace gave notice to quit, Mrs Camplin was given his house.

The council's tenants may have counted themselves lucky, but the rent was higher than for many of the 'very old and too closely spaced' private landlord cottages and paying it was a struggle. The council learned that a labourer named Clark and his family had been sleeping in their garden shed in Corporation Terrace during the summer so as to be able to let out the bedrooms in the house to visitors.

Defending himself, Mr Clark told the town clerk that his family still had full access to water and sanitation, but that he and his wife 'have to earn every shilling we can in the summer to look forward to the winter'. The council left the matter in the hands of the medical officer of health to decide what to do. All the signs are that Dr Cook was a humane man.

And so was the council, at least towards its employees. In November 1925, a council workman called Alfred Hallett (quite possibly gravel-cracking Hallett, the roadworker who in 1917 had got called up with the result that the young lady had been thrown from her trap when it slipped on his grit-free over-smooth road), had gone into the cottage hospital for an operation. He requested that the council make up the difference between his normal wage for a 44-hour week and the sum he received from the National Health Insurance. They agreed to do so for one month, saying they would review his case in December. They did so, and again next spring, and again in the summer. A year later in October 1926 Mr Hallett was still too ill to work, and the council was still making up his wages. But it was not a right: he had to ask.

Although the new tenants in Corporation Terrace seem to have been generally pleased with their new homes, there were inevitably a few teething problems. Less than two years after they moved in, two tenants claimed the dressers in their kitchens had collapsed, breaking crockery worth £2 in one case and £1 in the other. Builder Charlie Hallett agreed to re-fix the dressers but refused to pay them anything for the broken crockery. A third tenant complained that after 18 months in his house, it was about time someone put up a fence behind. One morning recently he had opened his back door to find a couple of horses gazing in at him.

The eight new council houses went little way to solving the general shortage of decent housing. Even the decrepit private rental housing was better than living with the in-laws, the only option for many young couples.

The council needed more land. Up the River Lym, above Higher Mill on the right, was an ideal site called Colway Mead. It belonged to Richard Henley Torbock who, following the death of Colonel Henry Henley, had inherited the title of Lord of the Manor of Lyme Regis and was now the principal landowner in the borough.

Richard was 23 years old, a lieutenant in the Royal Navy and, very conveniently, far away on active service in China. In August 1927 the council applied for a compulsory purchase order to buy 8.6 acres of his land at Colway Mead for housing.

The residents of Colway Lane, which would provide the sole means of access to the estate for vehicles to begin with, at once launched a petition in protest. A council estate on their doorstep would mean entirely the wrong sort of neighbours. By the end of the month, however, a counter-petition circulated throughout the town in favour of a new estate on Colway Mead had collected 181 signatures.

In January 1928 the Ministry of Health confirmed the order 'for the compulsory acquisition of Colway Mead for the purposes of Part III of the Housing Act 1925' which, one can safely assume, was for the building of houses. The Henley Estate solicitors responded by offering to sell the council instead the field above Corporation Terrace for £400 per acre, but the council declined. Then the Henley solicitors submitted a claim for £4,416 compensation for the depreciation the development would cause to the value of the lands adjoining Colway Mead. The Town Clerk replied that the council was unable to agree the claim, and required that the amount of any compensation be settled in the manner directed by the Acquisition of Land Act of 1919. The Henley Estate solicitors went quiet.

As for Lieutenant Torbock, he next popped up in 1953 as Commander Torbock, High Sheriff of Westmorland, and died in 1994 at the age of 90.

In February 1928 the council published its plan for the Colway Mead Estate. In the first phase there were to be 24 homes of '12 parlour-type and 12 non-parlour type houses'. The parlour-type were larger and would cost two shillings a week more. And, for the first time for council housing, the specification stated that tenders should include the cost of providing not just roads, sewers, water and gas but also 'electricity services'. There was no plan at that stage to provide individual houses with electricity, but the estate as a whole was to be wired to the mains.

By 1929 housing scheme for Colway Mead was under way and had expanded from 24 to 36 houses. The council decided not to let any of them until 15th September when they would all be ready and all the tenants could move in at once.

The new Colway Mead estate in late 1929.

The rents were set at 13s.6d per week for the 30 parlour-type and 11s.6d for now only six non-parlour houses. An amendment to reduce the rents to 12s.6d and 10s.6d was defeated. As the opening date approached, some prospective tenants must have realised how difficult it would be to afford the rents, and eleven withdrew. However their places were immediately filled by others. A rent collector, Mr Wheadon, was appointed for the Colway Mead and Corporation Terrace estates, to be paid a commission of 2½ per cent of the rents he collected.

The council wanted Colway Mead kept neat and tidy. The tenancy agreements stated no pigs to be kept on any part of the estate, no fowls within 40 feet of any dwelling house, and no clothes lines or other drying apparatus erected in front gardens. For ten Colway Mead allotments there were at once 15 applications.

The cost of the project came in more or less exactly on budget: £1,600 for the land, £2,000 for the roads, £550 for the sewers and £15,240 for the houses, or £423 each. For public lighting the council got a quote from the Devon Gas Association but chose electricity instead and erected seven lamp standards for a cost of £133 5s.9d. Also in September 1929, Charlie Camplin, who had now worked for the Electricity Department since June 1920, got a further rise from £2 10s.0d to £3 per week.

No-one had stopped to consider that one day residents of Colway Mead might be able to afford their own cars. A 1930 Wolsey Hornet cost £175, the equivalent of almost five years' rent for one of the larger houses, so there were no garages and the only access for occasional visiting vehicles was from the old Roman trackway on the far side, Colway Lane. On the town side, residents could only reach the estate over a stile from Woodmead Road. After a few weeks they complained it was 'a struggle for people with prams, etc', and the council instructed Surveyor Prescott to prepare drawings to replace the stile with a self-closing gate.

TWENTIES END

In January 1927 the BBC was constituted under royal charter and, the *Bridport News* told its readers, the Post Office in London was shortly to open a radio-telephone service with New York. 'Young women telephone operators, with voices of special quality, have been selected to work on the new service.' There would be a minimum charge of £15 for a conversation of up to three minutes, with each additional minute charged at £5.

In Lyme Regis, public conveniences were on the agenda. There were three: at the bottom of Broad Street in the Square, half way along the Marine Parade for ladies only, and behind the *Cobb Arms*. (There was also a primitive gent's at the end of the Cobb, which in those days emptied straight into the sea.) The lavatories were a source of municipal income, with the users of cubicles charged a penny a go. For the same cost as a one-minute telephone conversation with New York, you could spend a penny 1,200 times. In its budget for 1927 the council predicted an income from public lavatories of £149 0s.0d, or 35,760 visits.

The Ladies' on the Marine Parade

Since the previous summer, the new public lavatories in the Square had been fitted with electric lights, two for the gent's side and two for the ladies'. In February, the council had iron bars with spikes fitted on the cubicle partitions to deter poor but desperate users from climbing in. Also an indignant letter was received asking if something could be done to prevent young men from visiting the ladies' on the Marine Parade. The Town Clerk replied to the effect that the writer was living in a world of fantasy as those particular lavatories had been closed for more than a month. In June the council approved the appointment of Mrs R.Toms as ladies' lavatory attendant at 30s. a week.

In those days, wages were often negotiated individually rather than according to set scales. Early in 1927, Assistant Engineer Camplin got another rise of 10s. a week bringing his wage to £2 10s.0d, but his colleague Mr Mills got nothing and handed in his notice. The Senior Assistant, Horace Stone, was offered 5s. a week but he turned this down so the council then tried 10s. which he accepted. The Department also advertised a five-year apprenticeship at a starting wage of 5s. a week. Two boys applied and Les Sharley got it. To put these wages in context, the foreman in charge of all the borough's roads at that time earned £3 a week.

In March 1927 the council decided it wanted to turn George's Square into its second car park. This triangle of land off Coombe Street had been bequeathed to the town in 1908 by Alban Woodroffe's father. It was known locally as 'Cats' Park' and was obviously neglected as a Mr Gush wrote complaining that the shrubs planted by Alban Woodroffe in 1909 were now so large they were shutting out the light from his kitchen.

When he learned of the car park plan, the solicitor in charge of James Woodroffe's estate wrote objecting. The land had been given 'for a free public pleasure or recreation ground, or garden, and for no other purpose'. He also noted that the square has been kept locked in recent years because the council claimed that children who played there were destructive. Be that as it may, he said, the square should still be kept open for the general purpose for which it had been dedicated, if necessary under the surveillance of the police.

There were now, according to *Kelly's Directory*, two electricians in town and also, in response to the arrival of the BBC, 'Gordon Williams, wireless dealer' of Monmouth Street. In October the council gave one of its tenants in Corporation Terrace permission to erect 'a wireless pole' in the hedge behind his house.

Kelly's also names Mrs Nelly Raymond as 'proprietor of the cinematographic theatre' in the Assembly Rooms, suggesting that John Raymond had died, just too soon to marvel at the 'talkies', which first appeared in 1928*.

In September Mrs Raymond wrote asking for her lease on the Assembly Rooms to be renewed for a further three years. The council agreed in principle but made the renewal subject to a satisfactory report on the state of the building by the borough surveyor. Much of it was well over a hundred years old. Unfortunately when Surveyor Prescott's report appeared, it said the building was unsafe and a fire-risk. The council accepted his recommendation that it should be closed without delay.

Surveyor Prescott shared an office in the museum with the finance officer, Mr Cheeseworth. That summer the council had invested in providing them with a telephone. In November, because they complained the office paraffin stove was inadequate, the council splashed out further on an 'electric radiator' at a cost of £1 12s.6d (plus £2 10s.0d for the wiring and 2d an hour for current).

At about that time the Town Mill finally ceased grinding corn, ending an era that stretched back nearly 600 years. Its demise was by no means unique: from their heyday in the Victorian age when there were perhaps 60,000 across the country, Britain's water and windmills had gone into sharp decline as cheap imported grain and engine-powered roller-mills at the major ports stole their trade away.

It seems that for its last few years the Town Mill ground only animal feed, with the site mainly used by W.H.Pinney & Co as a depot for its coal merchant business. The best evidence for exactly when it ground to a halt came from Gerald Glyde of Charmouth. His father, a tenant farmer from Abbot's Wootton in the Marshwood Vale, used to send his barley and maize to Lyme for Oswald Fowler to mill.

---

* Before the 'talkies', most people in Britain had never heard an American accent and vice versa. This may have been why the Post Office needed 'young women telephone operators with voices of special quality' for its first transatlantic service.

In 1925 Gerald was sent to Alban Woodroffe's new grammar school on Hill Road 'because my father could pay'. For the first year he walked the three miles from the farm up to Penn Cross and then took the motor bus down into Lyme. Later his parents let him ride to school on his pony, stabling it during the day at the Town Mill 'because my father was a good customer of Mr Fowler's and, I think, my great grandmother was a Fowler of the same family'.

Early in 1927 the council started to build the new stretch of road out of Lyme, by-passing the steep haul up Timber Hill, on the land Alban Woodroffe had presented the previous autumn. Some navvies working on the road were billeted in the town and, Gerald remembers, had one day left their corduroy trousers to soak in the mill-leat, secured to a railing by their straps. He also remembers releasing the straps and watching the trousers go over the waterwheel. So it looks as though the mill was still working in the first half of 1927.

At the end of July 1927, Oswald Fowler wrote to the council asking if they would care to buy the Mill with its garage, stabling, stores and water rights. Asked for his advice, Engineer Brown said he thought the water rights would be of no practical use to the Electricity Department so the council replied to Oswald that it could not 'entertain the offer'.

Although Arthur Brown was probably right, the Town Mill with its mill house, yard and outbuildings right in the middle of town could be a very useful site for the council. Here also was the chance to re-unite it with the Malthouse generating station works. Whether the mill's waterpower could generate a few extra kilowatts of electricity was not really the point.

Oswald Fowler and William Pinney seem not to have realised this, because they employed an engineer to prepare a report on the Mill's potential waterpower. His report was presented to the Urban Committee in October.

'The measured flow of water in the current stream is equal to about 150 feet per minute. With this quantity and a fall of 13' 6', about 4 brake horsepower could be developed by a modern turbine. If the storage pond* was properly cleaned out, its estimated storage capacity is 35,000 cubic feet. The leat from the pond to the Mill is about 720 feet long and has a sectional area of about 8 feet. When full it would have a storage capacity of 5,760 cubic feet. The storage capacity of the pond and leat is therefore 40,760 feet (cubic). Assuming the power unit of, say 6 brake horse-power, was run with the current stream and reserves, they [the Electricity Department] could look to run it for nearly 4 hours.'

This did not convince the Electricity Committee but on 27th October the council applied to the Ministry of Health for the necessary sanction to borrow £1,500 to buy the Mill, 'the aim being to acquire if for the purpose of centralising the Council's services, including stores, garage and stables, and preserving the water rights for the Electricity Undertaking'. However, negotiations faltered and in January 1928 the Town Mill was offered for sale by auction.

The auction took place at Radford and Radford's offices in Broad Street but failed to attract any other buyers. After a pause, the council re-opened negotiations, but this time with the Midland Bank in Axminster – presumably Pinney & Co's creditors – and offered only £800 for the Mill. The bank accepted and the sale was agreed on 23rd October 1928.

The following spring the doorway linking the main part of the Mill to the miller's house was bricked up to create a separate residence, and the council spent £137 redecorating it ready for letting. Conveyance was finally completed in June and several local people put in bids for the tenancy. In November 1929, however, the council accepted the argument of Albert

---

* This 'storage pond' must have been the water stored upstream behind hatches for flushing the river. These stood up beyond Gosling Bridge by the old Silk Mill. In the 1920s, the council' paid Oswald Fowler £10 a year for flushing the river, suggesting the Mill's water-rights and responsibilities extended beyond the mill-leat to this 'pond'.

Boalch to let his family have the house for 12s.6d per week. Albert had just been appointed Corporation fitter and plumber at a salary of £3 a week, so this arrangement would put its own employee living on site to keep an eye on the new mill depot. As for the Mill itself, a plan was floated to install a turbine and larger battery there to supply the town from midnight to 7.00am, probably because of more complaints about the noise from the Malthouse. However, the council dropped the plan because of the cost, and for the next eight years the mill remained unused except as a dumping ground, its old iron waterwheel quietly rusting away.

Electricity consumption had been increasing steadily, from 29,710 units in the first quarter of 1927 to 40,830 by the last quarter of 1928. The picture was the same all over the country and the Electricity Commissioners were pressing small towns everywhere to discontinue generating their own current and plan to connect up to the national grid.* Through economies of scale this would reduce electricity prices for their consumers and regulate what remained a rather idiosyncratic – some might say chaotic – sector of the industry.

The council briefly considered the idea of importing power from Exeter. It dismissed it, ostensibly on grounds of the capital expense but quite possibly really because of the local jobs and independence that having one's own electricity undertaking conveyed. It also considered but rejected a proposal to reduce the power-rate of 4d a unit further to encourage its wider use 'in the mornings and in summer'. However, it did agree to allow eight of the town's hotels to illuminate their signs at the power-rate instead of the higher lighting-rate of a shilling a unit.

---

* The 1926 Electricity Act had actually given the Electricity Commissioners powers to close generating stations if it was cheaper to get the supply from a neighbouring undertaking or off the National Grid.

Unemployment must have been falling, temporarily as it turned out, for in June 1928 the local Poor Law administrators wrote to the council informing them that Lyme Regis Employment Office would be closed. Only eight men and one boy were claiming unemployment benefit, and claimants could attend the Axminster Office once a week instead. The council replied they felt there should be an office in the borough. The result of this correspondence is not recorded.

Gradually, house by house and street by street, homes further and further from the Malthouse were able to connect to electricity. 'A labourer, who was knocked off his ladder whilst endeavouring to free a cable on the new mains extension in Ware Lane, was conveyed to the Cottage Hospital.' In autumn 1928 the Electricity Commissioners gave the council permission to extend the mains over the county border to supply the whole village of Uplyme. The plan was to run them up along the river, over the fields and through the woods. The Ratepayers Association protested: 'It would be an act of pure vandalism to carry the mains to Uplyme across Middle Mill field on poles'. The following autumn Engineer Brown proudly informed the council that Uplyme parish church had been connected. Electrifying Uplyme had been a pet project of his. The poles in Middle Mill field are there to this day.

Mrs Raymond had surrendered the lease of her Assembly Rooms cinema, closed as unsafe, late in 1927 and what must have seemed a dazzlingly bright 200-watt lamp on a standard had been erected opposite the Rooms outside the public lavatories in the Square. In February 1928 a row broke out between the council and Mrs Raymond's solicitors about an unpaid bill for the generator they had supplied for the cinema which she claimed had never worked, but was working perfectly well for Mr Hardy who had rented the Drill Hall nearby and set up a cinema there.

Meanwhile the fate of the Assembly Rooms hung in the balance. In December the council decided to demolish them but then in January 1929 amended its decision to 'to repair and re-wire them'. Eventually in March it conducted a remarkably democratic postcard ballot on the Rooms' future. Should they be repaired and updated or demolished and the space used for an enlarged Cobb Gate car park? 295 residents voted to repair them but 458 voted for the car park, and their fate was sealed.

Summer 1929, from the *Bridport News*.

Also early in 1929 the police station moved from Coombe Street to a new brick building in Hill Road. The council spent £103 10s.6d having the old police station including its cells and the sergeant's cottage next door refurbished by Fire Chief Foxwell's building firm. In August they let the cottage to Mr Legg for 10s. and the police station and cells to Mr Broomfield for 13s. a week.

The old police station in Coombe Street today, with space above the door for 'Dorset Constabulary'.

The end of the 1920s more or less coincided with the end of the horse-drawn age stretching back thousands of years. Horses and carts did not vanish overnight, but in November 1929 the council overturned its previous decision to buy a new horse and instead bought its second lorry. The Lorry Purchase Sub-committee chose a Bean for £437, fitted with a body suitable for collecting refuse. And it decided that 'following the purchase of the new lorry, the horses, carts, and stable implements etc be sold at auction'. Their sale at auction by Radford & Radford in December raised just £52 0s.6d. 1929 was not really a horse-sellers' market.

A 1929 Bean 30-cwt refuse vehicle. Front-wheel brakes and a self-starter cost extra.

It also saw the end of the old method of calling out members of the fire brigade. The Bridport News explained that this was for 'the police to obtain the services of boys living near the old police station in Coombe Street, and these lads went the various firemen who were thus informed'. Now the police station had moved up to Hill Road this was no longer practical so a siren was erected at the Town Mill and a telephone installed in the mill house so that Albert Boalch, the council 'turnkey', could arrange to have the greatest possible pressure of water directed to a particular hydrant. In August 1929 Herbert Foxwell had retired as Water Bailiff after 40 years' service and Albert Boalch and Surveyor Prescott took over responsibility for Lyme water supply.

In his final annual report for the year 1929 Chief Fire Officer Foxwell wrote: 'As houses have been built in larger numbers towards the outskirts of the Borough, I would respectfully suggest that the Council should consider the question of providing a motor hose-cart or tender, as the time taken in conveying the appliances in hand-drawn hose-carts is considerable. Thanking you for the consideration you have shown me during the 26 years I have been in charge of the brigade. Yours faithfully, H E Foxwell. Chief Officer.'

From 31st December Captain Foxwell became Honorary Superintendent of the Brigade, Lieutenant Randall took over as chief officer, and the council agreed to install a telephone in his house too. However, it decided it could not yet afford a motorised fire-engine.

In his report for 1929 Medical Officer of Health Dr Cook wrote that there were 18 legitimate and one illegitimate birth in the town, which he estimated now had a population of 2,394. There were three certified midwives. The water supply continued to be generally insufficient in summer. 'Scavenging' (rubbish collection) was carried out by the council's new lorry, which would soon entirely replace the horse carts previously used. Unlike the carts, the new lorry was covered and this should 'reduce the risk of disseminating disease'. The River Lym was being flushed twice a week in summer and, when necessary, once a week in winter, to remove rubbish thrown in at night 'which is unavoidable when a river passes by the walls of a poor class neighbourhood'.

He continued, 'The housing scheme at Colway Mead was completed during 1929 and the 36 houses occupied as soon as they were ready. Overcrowding in the town is now almost completely relieved, and landlords have taken the opportunity to renovate some of the older houses. However, in a town where work is scarce, there is considerable demand for property which commands a rental much lower than those of the modern homes at Colway Mead and Corporation Terrace.'

During the year Dr Cook said he had inspected 17 dwelling houses which were 'not in all respects fit for human habitation', 12 factories and 26 workshops. In the latter he found a number of defects but all of these had been remedied. National Rat Week in November had been a great success thanks to the use of dogs and ferrets at the town tip. Not counting excursion steamers, seven coasting vessels had entered the port during the year.

As for the Electricity Department, the council extended its formal thanks to Arthur Brown and his staff for maintaining the town's electricity supply during an influenza outbreak, agreed to supply Mr O'Neil with current for his Peerless weighing machine on the Marine Parade at the lower power-rate of 4d a unit, rejected a suggestion to scrap the two-rate tariff for power & lighting in favour of a single price, and spent £768 upgrading the batteries in the Malthouse to 8,333 amp/hours in the hope that they could provide the town's entire electricity quietly from bedtime through the night. However for some reason – perhaps to register their disapproval of Communism – although the Soviet Union had reduced the price of its petroleum by 1½d a gallon, the Electricity Committee recommended to the Council that it 'do not buy Soviet oil' to run the Malthouse generators.

1929 ended in Lyme Regis with record sales of electricity, in neighbouring Bridport with the arrival finally of its first public electricity supply, and in America with the Wall Street Crash.

ALL RIGHT FOR SOME

The 1930s began with a series of gales stripping slates from cottages in the town and the Electricity Committee asking Lyme's two headmasters to recommend a suitable boy to fill a second apprenticeship at the Malthouse. They suggested six, three were called for interview and Stanley Stocker got the job.

At about the same time, the council granted the Lyme Regis Silver Band permission to use an upstairs room for band practice at its new depot at the Town Mill, and install an electric light and gas fire there. To complete these luxurious arrangements they asked Surveyor Prescott to provide a temporary staircase (in place of the ladder) so the band could safely reach the room.

It was also agreed to provide free electricity for the Marine Parade illuminations during a planned three-day visit in July by *HMS Rodney* ('the finest battleship in the Navy') and for *The Daily Express* to be allowed to arrange community singing on Gun Cliff in September as part of the Daily Express National Community Singing Movement. The Movement was an attempt to raise national morale during these dark days of the Depression and also, possibly, to promote sales of the recently published *Daily Express Community Song Book*.

Unemployment in Britain reached two million in 1930. To create jobs in the building industry, the Ministry of Health allowed local councils to lend builders up to 50 per cent of the construction costs of new houses until they were sold, at a fixed 5 1/4 per cent interest. To encourage job-creating projects that did not produce income, for instance new roads, the Ministry would itself pay 75 per cent of the interest on council loans as an 'unemployment grant'.

Lyme Regis Council decided to offer eleven building plots fronting Colway Lane to private developers. These formed a small slice of the 8.6 acres at Colway Mead it had compulsorily purchased from Lieutenant Torbock for £1,600 in 1927. As well as the jobs the development would create, the sale should make the council £720. It priced the plots at 30s. per foot (0.3m) frontage, or 40s. per foot for the corner sites. The conditions of sale were that only one house be erected per plot, and that the building-cost be at least £450 per house.

Nearby, on the Colway Mead council estate, eight more houses were about to be built for £360 each. These would bring the total on the estate to forty four, but an argument developed between the council and the Ministry of Health, which was providing the necessary loan.

The council had awarded the contract worth £2,878 to two local builders, Charlie Hallett and a Mr Cooper. Somehow or other the two had managed to submit exactly identical quotes and agreed to share the project. However, an out-of-town builder called Ramsay had quoted £14 per house less and complained to the Ministry. The council defended its position, saying it had chosen the local contractors because they were known and reliable, but the Minister insisted Ramsay's tender be accepted. A lower price would result in lower rents, and low rents were the whole point of council housing.

The council delayed replying for some months. Eventually it informed the Minister that, regrettably, the original quotes were now out of date so it would be forced to invite the various contractors to submit fresh tenders. Second time around Messrs Hallett and Cooper again won the contract, this time also on price.

15 ALL RIGHT FOR SOME

That summer, while work began on the eight new council houses, Surveyor Prescott unveiled a plan to build a further 30 on Colway Mead, bringing the total to seventy-four. In this surge of self-confidence, the council reduced all its tenants' rents by 6d a week, gave Mr Pocock permission to install a beehive and, on 30th July under the heading 'Eugenic Sterilisation of mentally defective persons', recommended acceptance of the principle of the sterilisation of the mentally unfit.

Modernisation was in the air. In London the BBC made its first experimental television broadcasts. In Lyme at his new cinema in the Drill Hall Mr Hardy was showing the first 'talkie' seen in town. *Behind the Curtain* was 'a real talkie masterpiece and a marvel of perfect speech', said *The Bridport News*. A growing number of residents owned wireless sets. Those living by the Malthouse complained that the generators there caused interference to their reception so Arthur Brown installed 'condensers' in the works. These were so effective that the council offered to sell them to anyone in town with a private generator for 9s.6d each.

Elsewhere, the council purchased three automatic towel machines for the public lavatories for 37s.6d each and introduced residents' parking permits (except for July, August and September) at the Cobb Gate car-park for 5s. a year. It also voted by eight to three to invest in two telephones: one for its Malthouse generating station and one direct to the bedroom of Chief Fire Officer Randall. (The rest of the brigade was called by a hand-operated siren at the Town Mill.) It granted Mr Taylor of Ozone Terrace permission to attach a wireless aerial to the corner of Cobb Lodge, but an application by the British Photomatron Trading Co to erect a photographic kiosk of 20 feet by 15 feet (6m x 4.5m) near the Cobb was refused.

Cobb Gate car-park on the site of the demolished Assembly Rooms in the early 1930s, with the Cobb in the distance beyond.

In December 1930 Dorset County Council voted to accept a tender of £18,734 from Charlie Hallett to build a permanent grammar school on a site above the Uplyme Road. This would replace its temporary home in the army huts on Hill Road, and had been Alban Woodroffe's aim ever since he persuaded the county to give the town its school.

It was a hard run debate. County Councillor Cole argued that the existing huts were adequate. 'The time is not one for luxuries. We must go steadily. If for £400 we can put the school in order, we should not spend £20,000 for a new one.' However Alban Woodroffe won the day. His son Rex, who was also now a county councillor, appealed to the members 'to give Lyme Regis a school worthy of the town'. Alban, the chairman of the county education committee, was blunt. 'If you don't accept this tender, it will knock from me all my interest in educational work.' That seems to have swung the meeting: the council voted to accept the tender by 32 votes to 23 and Alban laid the foundation stone on 29th April 1931.

There were now 352 private and business electricity consumers in Lyme – about a third of the town. Between them they had 503 meters, suggesting that by now about 40 per cent were using electricity for purposes other than just lighting, and had had their premises wired with separate power circuits so that they could benefit from the lower 4d-per-unit power rate.

In his report for 1930, Dr Cook estimated the population of Lyme at 2,394 and that the number of dwellings had increased from about 450 in 1921 to 770. Of seventeen houses he had inspected, two were unfit and nine not in all respects fit for human habitation. He ended:

> A further eight houses were built in Colway Mead. It is impossible to give statistics to show the result already showing in improved health and what I can only describe as well-being, but it is plainly manifest to anyone working among the people of the borough. The fact that every front garden on this estate is cultivated as a flower garden shows that pride and pleasure are taken in the improved housing conditions afforded.

In January 1931 a businessman from down the coast in Seaton approached the council with an offer to erect an amusement park in the Langmoor Gardens overlooking the Cobb. He promised electric motor rides, shooting galleries, automatic machines and a 50-foot-high tower. And at night the whole plateau would be illuminated by electric lights until the park closed at 10.30pm. And on top of all this he was willing to pay the council a rent of £200 a year, and 'was sure the amusements would be a credit, not a drawback to the town'. The council replied coldly that it could not entertain his application.

In March a petition from ten local ice-cream vendors complained that some London firm called T. Wall & Sons had been placing 'ice-cream barrels' on the sea front. Unless the council took action, the local traders would be forced to resort to similar tactics. The council replied that it would call the matter to the attention of the police.

The mayor's macebearer and town crier, Walter Abbott, had won the National Town Crier Championship of England and Wales in 1930. On the suggestion of the Advertising Committee, it was agreed to host the national championships in Lyme that summer, on the Cobb. 'In spite of inclement weather, the attendance was over 1,000.' Walter won for the second year running and was presented with a framed copy of the council minutes congratulating him, copied on vellum and sealed with the corporate seal.

Councillor Emmett reported that an elderly couple called Newberry, who occupied one of the Marder Almshouses, were ill and wished to be allowed to have their granddaughter aged 13 to stay with them. Permission was granted. But an application from a Mr Dunstan, 'a complete invalid', for permission to drive his pony-drawn bath-chair along the traffic-free Marine Parade to visit his friends was refused, and a motion to purchase a motor lawn-mower for the Langmoor Gardens was rejected by six votes to five.

The obligatory bathing tents on the beach in the 1930s with the *Bay Hotel* and Langmoor Gardens behind.

In July the RSPCA asked for permission to erect and maintain a lethal gas chamber for unwanted dogs and cats. It would be sited behind the garage at the council's depot near the gas works. There was some months' delay while the council and RSPCA considered who would be responsible for operating it, but eventually the council gave consent. The question of responsibility seems to have been solved by making the lethal chamber self-service. Older residents remember a coin-operated gas oven in which the user placed the animal. After a suitable delay, the body was removed and taken to the nearby gas-works where it was incinerated in one of the furnaces.

Despite the relentless increase in electricity sales – up to 46,243 units in the first quarter of 1931 from 39,0504 the year before – the Electricity Department's books were showing a worrying loss. The 1930 accounts had the debit balance of the revenue account growing from £413 6s.7d in January to £1,550 3s.0d in October. Figures for 1931 had not yet appeared but councillors were alarmed.

On 1st June 1931 Councillor Washer, seconded by Alderman Bragg, slipped in a motion amidst unrelated matters: 'That the council endeavour to get in touch with an Electrical Company with a view to disposing of the Council's Electricity Undertaking.' The resolution was passed unanimously.

At the next meeting in July, Colonel Hynes, who was the chairman of the Electricity Committee, 'declared that the decision to sell the undertaking was reached at the last meeting, without practically any discussion, and by a more or less catch-vote. Enquiries had been made by outside individuals but the matter was still in a totally undigested state.' The Town Clerk reported that seven potential buyers had approached him for more details and copies of the undertaking's accounts. He had also received a letter from the Electricity Commissioners. They had told him that before the Corporation took any further action, it must discuss 'various aspects of the matter' with the Commissioners. He had arranged a meeting.

Why someone took a closer look at the Electricity Department's books is unclear. Perhaps it was the requests for more information from potential buyers, or preparing for the meeting with the Electricity Commissioners. In any event, on 19th October Colonel Hynes informed the Electricity Committee of a serious accounting error. £1,089 1s.8d due from consumers had not been brought forward in the books, and the bills for that sum had never been sent out. They had been now, by Arthur Brown working late with a temporary clerk.

On 30th October a special council meeting was called 'in committee' – their way of excluding the press. Mayor Baker told councillors it had emerged that Mr Cheeseworth, the borough accountant and financial officer, had failed to write up the Electricity Consumers' ledger for the past year. Moreover, what he had written up earlier contained 'a number of errors'. The mayor and Colonel Hynes had suspended Mr Cheeseworth from all Electricity Department affairs with immediate effect, and asked for his resignation.

A week later at 10.15am on 5th November, Frederick Cheeseworth said goodbye to his wife and three small children, had a whisky and went to the office. At 11 o'clock he had another 'with a commercial'. On the way to lunch at *The London Inn* he had a gin and bitter, and on returning to the office had another whisky. All this he told the court when, at the end of November, he appeared to deny a charge of driving a motor-car to the danger of the public whilst under the influence of drink. Three local witnesses, including Councillor Emmett, came forward to testify that he had been sober up to five o'clock that afternoon.

Which was odd because at 5.25pm he crashed into a car driven by Miss Phoebe Waterfield on the road between Honiton and Exeter 20 miles away. He was on the wrong side of the road and Miss Waterfield only managed to avoid a head-on collision by swerving sharply across the road to the right. Witnesses at the scene said Mr Cheeseworth was so drunk that he had to cling on to the mudguard of his car to save himself from falling over.

'His voice was thick.' 'There was a strong smell of drink.' 'I did not see him walk without catching hold of a car,' they said. When P.C. Stevens asked for his name his reply was inaudible. When asked to spell it, he retorted crossly, 'Cheese, common or garden cheese!'

According to the *Bridport News*, the case occupied Ottery St Mary magistrates for 'upwards of five hours'. In the end, despite pleas that it would end his career, Cheeseworth was found guilty. He was fined £5 for dangerous driving, £20 for being under the influence of drink, ordered to pay £7 2s.9d costs, and his driving licence was suspended for two years.*

Back in Lyme Regis, the council agreed to advertise for a replacement borough accountant at a salary of £260 a year, the advertisement to stress that the work included a good deal of routine calculation. The Reverend Eyre offered to try to correct the Electricity Department's books but, after some deliberation, the council realised it needed a professional to sort out the mess, and engaged a Bridport chartered accountant called Mr Burrough.

In December 1931 Mr Burrough joined the Electricity Committee for their meeting. He said that, apart from the unsent bills, 'some serious omissions and discrepancies in the accounts have come to light'. The tone suggests he suspected dishonesty. He added that the work had taken far longer than he had anticipated so he would charge the council for the actual time and expenses incurred. On a happier note, however, his draft accounts to the end of March 1931 indicated not a loss but a surplus of £390 for the year.

There was also a letter from the Electricity Commissioners saying that 'in view of the latest and more favourable financial results, they considered the Corporation should continue the distribution of electricity in the borough'. The plan to sell the undertaking was shelved.

*In those days you needed a driving licence even though the driving test was not to be introduced until June 1935.

Meanwhile back in the world of dreams, it was reported to the council that someone had unscrewed the lamp-cover in the men's lavatory on the Marine Parade and stolen the lamp. The matter was called to the attention of the police.

On the subject of drink, Mr Cheeseworth was by no means the only one in the area with a problem. Of 32 persons proceeded against for being drunk and disorderly in nearby Bridport in 1931, seven were found to have been drinking methylated spirits.

In the 25th December issue of the *Bridport News*, a story appeared headed 'Roadster in the Pantry'. It told how, at the *Black Dog Inn* in Uplyme, a hungry tramp or 'roadster' called James Anderson of no fixed abode was seized by Percy Stapleforth the landlord's son as he emerged from the pantry with a pound of butter and a leg of chicken in his hands. In the scuffle that ensued, Anderson threw the chicken and butter into the roadway but Mr and Mrs Stapleforth and Percy 'detained the accused until a police constable arrived'.

Superintendent Willcocks told the court that Anderson had ten or eleven previous convictions for housebreaking or stealing. Although his last offence was committed back in 1925, the Bench sentenced him to six months in prison.

In January 1932 the council thanked Arthur Brown for all his extra work sorting out the Electricity department's finances and paid him a gratuity of £10. However, by April there were still 90 electricity consumers refusing to pay the arrears run up when 'the late Financial Officer failed to render accounts' and the council had to threaten to take them to court. It also sent round a general sharp reminder of the need to pay electricity bills on time, and introduced a 5 per cent discount for those who paid within seven days and 2½ per cent for payment within fourteen.

In April Mr Burrough finished checking all the borough's accounts and reported that a total of £307 16 9d was missing, including £124 18 10d from the Deck-chair Letting Account. The council managed to recover £200 from an insurance policy and must have been pursuing Mr Cheeseworth for the rest because in June he wrote with a cheque for £100 'which my wife's parents have kindly provided as a loan'. He added that he would re-pay the remaining few pounds as soon as he found employment, but the council replied accepting the £100 cheque as final settlement.

Apart from the drunken driving incident, none of this affair ever appeared in the press. Of the £300 recovered, the council gave one third to the Electricity Department and two-thirds to the Urban Fund to make up for the missing money from their deck-chairs.

Elsewhere in town, now that Chief Fire Officer Herbert Foxwell had retired, the station stores needed to be relocated (maybe on Mrs Foxwell's insistence), and were moved from Herbert's shed to one next door belonging to 'Spike' Hardy of the cinema at a rent of £10 a year.

On 21st May 1932 there was a severe storm. *The Bridport News* described it as 'the worst experienced since 1894'. Two cottages up river were flooded because, the residents claimed, the new concrete bridge near the Jordan Mill laundry had been built too low. At the allotments 'a great quantity of soil' was washed away and four allotment holders, including electricity pioneer T.G.Hains, requested a reduction in their rents for loss of crops etc. This was refused but Surveyor Prestcott arranged for a load of new topsoil to be delivered to the allotment gate. The council also decided to offer a prize for the best and second best-kept allotment, to be judged by Mr Shellabeer, head gardener at Major Allhusen's Pinhay estate.

Also in May the newly built grammar school on the Uplyme Road was opened by the Earl of Shaftesbury. Alban Woodroffe had had it designed by the same architect he used for the alterations to Rhode Hill. At the opening ceremony, he presented builder Charlie Hallett with an inscribed silver cigarette box.

In the same week an experimental putting green opened in the Langmoor Gardens.

Who performed the opening ceremony if there was one is not recorded, but players were charged 4d a go and the council finally decided to buy a motor-mower for the Gardens from Mr Bragg at a price, including discount for cash, of £31-10-0d. Down at the Town Mill, attention was called to the damage occasioned by 'children etc' playing at the council depot so it was decided to erect a 6ft high corrugated iron fence with pointed tops. In an amendment, the words 'corrugated iron' were removed.

There were now well over a million motor vehicles on the roads of Britain. At the bottom of Broad Street opposite the enlarged Cobb Gate car park was the yard and offices of Bradford & Sons, coal and general merchants. That year they agreed to sell their site to be re-developed into the town's second car-park. The council was keen, partly because 'an additional car park would be a fine advertisement for the town', partly because with a new car park they could stop people parking along the Marine Parade and let out the space the more profitably for visitor facilities, and partly because building it would provide work for the town's unemployed. The parking fee would be 6d a time, or one sixtieth of the weekly wages of a Dorset farm worker, set in 1931 by the Agricultural Wages Committee in Dorchester at £1 10s.0d a week.

1932 was the depth of the Depression. Unemployment peaked at 2,750,000, and the Government introduced the 'means test' and cut the 'dole' by 10 per cent. In Lyme Regis in November, *The Bridport News* reported, 'There are something like 100 workless men locally, and in a number of cases the plight of the families is pitiable'.

The council met to see what was to be done. It established an Unemployment Committee to try to bring forward public projects to give men work, and also show them 'that the council was not unmindful of their position'. 'Every man on the dole locally,' declared Alderman Baker, 'would rather wear out than rust out.' The projects the committee proposed included the new car park, increasing the town's water supply and improving the roads. However, Mayor Worth admitted, 'If the council has not the necessary money, I do not see what can be done to help the unemployed'.

Some work, however, was found. The borough surveyor reported that the council houses in Corporation Terrace and the earliest ones in Colway Mead now needed repainting. The council decided to employ its own painter at a fixed wage. When it advertised the post, thirteen men applied. Mr Legg of Coombe Street got the job.

POWER TO THE PEOPLE

The jolt the Cheeseworth affair gave the council turned out to be a blessing. In their letter, the Electricity Commissioners urged the council 'to foster development of demand by introducing schemes of assisted wiring and the hire purchase of electrical apparatus, and a more appropriate two-part tariff for domestic supplies', which meant lowering prices. Until now, Lyme Regis had been content to supply rather expensive electricity to a few hotels and other businesses and to its richer residents' homes. The Commissioners' message was simple: it was time to set about selling as much electricity as you can to as many consumers as possible.

Behind their advice lay a government policy. This was that for Britain to develop a modern competitive economy, it needed to produce cheap electricity. There were six hundred or so independent municipal and private electricity undertakings in the country, and to produce cheaper electricity each company needed to sell more, and not just in the evenings to the rich for lighting. It was now in the national interest for Mrs Smith in Corporation Terrace to get connected, and to start using an electric iron as well as lights.

Assisted wiring schemes helped poorer families connect to the mains by spreading the cost of wiring up a house over a number of years. The average price of installing a simple lighting system had fallen from about £19 in 1919 to as little as five or six pounds in the 1930s; even less when a group of houses were wired at the same time. Nevertheless, that sum still represented two or more weeks' wages for many families. It was beyond their means.

Typically an assisted wiring scheme worked by requiring the householder to put down a small deposit to get connected. They would then repay the rest of the installation cost over several years by paying a small surcharge on top of the standard price per unit. At the end of the 1920s, a third of Britain's electricity companies were already operating assisted wiring schemes. By 1936 the figure had risen to 84 per cent.

In Lyme Regis for its financial year to 31st March 1932, the Electricity Department had made a profit of £807 10s.4d. The council's initial step to foster demand was to cut electricity prices for the first time in more than a decade. The lighting-rate went down from 12d (a shilling) to 10d a unit and the power-rate from 4d to 3d.

It also accepted the Electricity Commissioners' recommendation to consider introducing an assisted wiring scheme. To that end it asked the local electrical contractors to conduct a survey in Colway Mead to see how many council tenants might want to connect up. And to show it really meant business, it ordered that the corporation lorry 'be lettered to advertise electricity' and authorised Arthur Brown to buy the finance office's old Remington typewriter for the Electricity Department for £4 10s.0d.

In November the contractors reported back. With only one exception, every Colway Mead tenant would be willing to become an electricity consumer, 'providing they do not have to pay for the installation cost in advance'.

In December 1932 Arthur Brown produced an estimate that to wire up the council's stock of 74 houses on the Colway Mead estate and the twenty eight houses in Corporation Terrace with 'between 4 and 6½ lighting points per house depending on size' (half a point probably meant a two-way switch for the stairs), it would cost £1,128 0s.8d, or just over £11 per house.

On 19th December the council resolved to introduce the assisted wiring scheme. Consumers would be charged 2d above the standard rate for lighting and 1d for power 'until the actual cost of installation has been met'. The council applied for a loan of £2,500 from the Ministry of Health, to be divided £1,500 for wiring houses, £500 to buy slot meters and £500 for the costs of mains and services.

A 1930s advertisement by the Electricity Development Association.

Not surprisingly the local gas company, the Devon Gas Association Ltd, was none too happy with the news. It had just finished laying gas mains through Colway Mead. In January 1933 it wrote to the council to complain. It had supplied gas to the houses specifically at their request so if its fittings were now to be replaced by electricity, it should be paid compensation. The council replied that it was only providing electricity because its tenants had requested it, and so 'could not entertain any question of compensation'. In any case, as the current was being installed for lighting purposes only, the Company would still have the advantage of supplying gas for geysers,* stoves and coppers.

The council invited tenders for wiring its 103 council houses with a total of 611 lights. Five contractors submitted quotes and it decided to divide the work between them, 'the apportionment based on the number of local men employed'. Gordon Williams the wireless dealer and Mr James got 31 houses each; Mr Larcombe and Mr Samson 18, and Mr Holgate five. They were to be paid 17s. per light; on average just over £5 per house. Also, 'as a further means of finding employment', it was decided to lay the mains in Colway Mead underground if the necessary loan from the Ministry could be obtained.

By June 1933, 60 of the council's tenants had returned their completed application forms and Engineer Brown was instructed to arrange for their homes to be wired forthwith. The

* Geyser *n BrE* An apparatus used in kitchens, bathrooms etc for heating water by gas.

council decided that applications from non-council tenants would also be considered. In their case, however, the householder had to make a small down-payment as well as paying for current at the surcharge rate until the cost had been paid off. The initial deposit was 5s.or four lights. 'My mother paid 7s.6d because she also wanted a light with a two-way switch on the stairs,' one resident recalls.

To put these events in Lyme in context, 1932 was the year when Piccadilly Circus was first lit by electricity, King George V made the first Christmas Day broadcast across the Empire from the BBC, reading a speech written for him by Rudyard Kipling, and Ghandi was arrested for arguing that British Rule in India was not ideal. In 1933 Hitler was elected to power.

There was a whiff of revolution nearer home. The large numbers of men tramping the highways of England in search of work could find themselves admitted to the local workhouse or 'public assistance institution' as since 1930 they were called. Sometimes their admission was voluntary; at others they were detained by the local magistrates. Either way it was not a pleasant experience but they did get food and roof before being sent on their way.

The nearest former workhouse to Lyme Regis was in Axminster, and in January 1933 it narrowly escaped a riot. Never in the long proud history of this workhouse had 'such a disturbance been witnessed within its precincts as occurred there about 10 o'clock on Thursday morning', reported the *Bridport News*.

'Overnight, between 40 and 50 casuals had been accommodated in the wards, situated immediately inside the main entrance gates. Something like half of the number of these men had been detained for two nights in accordance with an Order recently made by the Devon Public Assistance Committee. The remainder of the casuals were admitted on Wednesday morning.'

The *Bridport News* explained that because of overcrowding, about half the men had had to sleep on the floors of the wards 'with only one blanket each to cover them on an extremely cold night'. They had not been supplied with 'their proper quantity of tea' and those who had got a bed complained that the straw in their bed-ticks (mattresses) was 'fusty'.

The report continued, 'Thus dissatisfied and with their tempers frayed, the men congregated in the main drive where they were harangued by three agitators. They sang the *"Red Flag"* and threatened to smash up the place if they were not at once discharged.'

The situation became ugly. Unable to cope with this 'riotous mob', the Master sent for the Chairman of the Guardians Committee. 'The casuals lined the main entrance and allowed his car to pass.' After consulting with the Master, 'the Chairman, acting in his own responsibility ordered the discharge of the whole of the casuals, whether they had been detained for two nights or not. Muttering dissatisfaction at their treatment, the casuals dispersed. Thus further trouble was avoided.' Later, Major Allhusen of Pinhay and other members of the committee agreed that there was something radically wrong with the system 'for casuals to be detained for two nights against their will and without the necessary accommodation'.

Back in Lyme Regis, in his report for 1932 Chief Fire Officer Randall once again raised the need for a motor fire engine. 'Houses have been built in large numbers towards the outskirts of the Borough and it is not fair to ask members [of the brigade] to push a loaded hose cart some distance and then get to work on a fire.' In March 1933 the Finance Committee relented and bought a second-hand 35-horse-power London Fire Brigade tender 'in splendid condition' for £50 plus £2 10s.0d for delivery. It had been built in 1921 by Dennis Bros of Guildford.

An early 1920s Dennis fire engine of the type bought for Lyme.

The value of the motor fire engine was demonstrated in July when Dr Lancaster's house in Colway Lane caught fire. Captain Randall reported, 'The brigade arrived within seven minutes of the call and, with the aid of the emergency water tank on the engine, commenced operations immediately thus saving the house from being a total loss'. He estimated the loss sustained at only £157, from a total value of house and contents of £4,000.

In recognition of all his work for the town, the council agreed to present Alban Woodroffe with the Freedom of Lyme Regis. In March 1933 Mayor George Worth sounded him out as to the manner in which he would like the honour to be bestowed. 'Mr Woodroffe does not wish for anything elaborate', he reported back, so the council decided to forego the party but instead gave him his presentation address inscribed on vellum.

For its summer 1933 season, the council ordered 12,000 adults bathing tickets, 15,000 deck chair tickets and 15,000 tickets for the Cobb Gate car park. It authorised the harbour-master to purchase four caps for the attendants to be employed that season, and prepared for income from six new tennis courts built on the site of the former grammar school on Hill Road. They would be let for half-a-crown (2s.6d) an hour. The old army huts were refurbished for community used and renamed the Woodmead Halls.

At the start of June, applications were sought for the posts of deck-chair and putting-green attendants for the Langmoor Gardens. They would be paid 30s. a week plus 5 per cent commission on takings. Ten men applied for the chairs and eight for the putting-green. Mr Jones and Mr Wright got the jobs, while Mrs Toms was reappointed ladies' lavatory attendant in preference to four other applicants.

Some council tenants were struggling to pay their rents. A notice to quit was issued to Mr Cozens at 26 Corporation Terrace whose arrears had grown to £6 18s.0d. However, he was told that, if he could 'substantially reduce' them, the notice might be withdrawn. In June 1933 Mrs Cozens wrote to the town clerk saying she hoped to pay off the greater part of the debt by the second week in July as she was expecting 'visitors' – summer paying guests – and her husband was now back in work.

Also in June, notices to quit were threatened on two neighbours in Colway Mead where 'a quarrel developed into a disturbance'. The town clerk wrote warning that any repetition of such conduct would result in their eviction.

In August 1933 Mr Robinson, a holidaymaker from Birmingham, wrote to complain. For the family's holiday, he had booked two weeks in an apartment at number 6 Coombe Street, the house next to 'Electricity Cottage'. After a week, however, they had been driven to find alternative accommodation because of the noise from the Malthouse generating station at night. He felt he was entitled to compensation. Council minutes do not record its response.

Also that summer the Electricity Committee raised Junior Engineer Les Sharley's wages to £2 a week. He had finished his five years' apprenticeship and might well have been expected to leave to find better-paid employment elsewhere, but Arthur Brown persuaded the Committee 'to retain him rather than engage a new man at a higher salary'. The council also further reduced the price of current for lighting to 9d and power to 2½d. And it agreed to spend 'not more than £35 installing a new Triplex kitchen range', and hot and cold water upstairs, at Arthur Brown's house. Electricity Cottage thus became the first house in Coombe Street with a bathroom with running hot water.

In his report for 1933 Dr Cook said that after many years of an inadequate supply, 'your town now has an ample supply of pure water'. There were 22 births, but deaths were down to 34 from 40 in the previous year when there had been an exceptionally severe epidemic of measles that had killed four people. There had also been less rubbish thrown in the river, possibly because one riverside householder had been successfully prosecuted.

National Rat Week was particularly energetically promoted that year with a distribution of posters and special displays in shop windows. Poisoned bait and biscuits were distributed free. During the year Dr Cook had taken five samples of milk, of which one was adulterated and the vendor prosecuted and fined. One new case of tuberculosis had been notified. The patient had died.

Dr Cook had found eight houses unfit for human habitation. This was quite a rise on previous years suggesting that, unless he had been less rigorous, the official standard for acceptable housing had been raised. He reported that two of the unfit houses had been demolished with the owners' agreement; the others would be dealt with 'under the Slum Clearance Act'. (This does not exist: he must have meant the 1930 Housing Act.)

At the start of 1934, there was a burglary off the Sidmouth Road at a bungalow known as Knapps Lodge. It had taken place, the *Bridport News* told readers, on Saturday night while the occupants, Mr and Mrs Keeley, were in bed. 'The intruders entered through the scullery window, which had inadvertently been left open. They helped themselves to eatables from the larder, and also a purse with money and a pipe and tobacco pouch'. What is striking is the prominence in the story given to the theft of the food. It sees that in the mid-1930s, burglars were still sometimes driven by hunger.

In March 1934, Gordon Williams, the electrician and wireless dealer in Coombe Street, sued Mrs Rosanne Driver for £24 4s.4d, which he claimed she owed him for some wiring work and a wireless set. Before the case got going in the County Court in Axminster, Mrs Driver handed over £20. However, Mr Williams was resolute in his pursuit of the rest.

Mrs Driver claimed Mr Williams had supplied her in May 1933 with a 1933 model wireless. However, she had specified she wanted 'an up-to-date model', and as that one had been superseded later that year by the 1934 model, she claimed the set Mr Williams had supplied was out of date. She also said that the switches for the wiring he installed were 'terrible' and had not been used in electrical installations for 20 years. Judge Lindley found for Gordon Williams and awarded him the balance of £4-4-0d plus costs, but he deducted £1 from the award as he seems to have had some sympathy with Mrs Driver's opinion of the switches.

In the summer of 1934, the council considered a query from the Sun Bathing Club about 'whether any part of the beach was enclosed for men and women to sun bathe nude'. Councillor Camplin said this was 'a disgraceful suggestion'. Alderman Wiscombe on the other hand was keen that the council 'should not be hasty in regard to this matter'. Council minutes do not record the outcome, but all the evidence suggests that councillors sided with Killjoy Camplin.

The news from the newly-built grammar school was that by Prize Day there were 122 pupils, but the great bulk of them were under fifteen and only five were sixteen. However, Miss Carson and Miss Slaney had taken a group of ten girls to Belgium at Easter, including to Ypres, Hell Fire Corner, Hill 60 and the Menin Gate. The group had been given a civic reception and had 'amusing experiences with their half fledged French and the Belgians' half-fledged English'. And, the headmaster stressed, the trip had not cost the ratepayers a penny. Next month Mr Blunt would be taking a group of boys for a fortnight to Norway.

Elsewhere in Lyme that summer, the Women's Institute held an evening picnic. 'A party of 20 started off at 7 p.m. by motor coach for Gittisham Common', reported the *Bridport News*. 'A competition for the best picnic supper for 6d had quite a number of entries. The first prize went to Mrs Lane and the second to Mrs Clark. Next a game, "Who would I like to be and why," caused much amusement, nearly all the members mentioning "film stars". One member, however, thought it would be good to be Lady Astor, as she does "get a move on". A cricket match was played on the Common, and afterwards there was a very happy ride home via Honiton, the journey being completed about 10 p.m.'

Back in January 1934, the council proposed a five-year slum clearance plan for the town. This identified about thirty dirty damp cramped old houses that needed either to be demolished or compulsorily improved. The 1933 Housing Act had temporarily stopped government loans for new council house building, but it still allowed councils to borrow if what they were building replaced part of the national programme of slum-clearance.

In Lyme Regis the first slums due to be demolished were known as Jordan Cottages owned by Edwin Wallis, and there were more at Mill Green, Silver Street and Sherborne Lane. To re-house the tenants from Jordan Cottages, the council invited tenders to build four more three-bedroom houses on the last remaining plots in Corporation Terrace. Emmett & Co won with a bid of £1,366.

With its teeth now into slum clearance, the council next turned its eyes to the western beach beyond the Cobb where the famous cement works had been standing derelict since 1914. The site belonged to Lord of the Manor Richard Torbock, the young lieutenant whose land at Colway Mead the council had compulsorily purchased in 1927. In May 1934 it condemned the cement works' two tall chimneys as dangerous, and ordered their demolition. Local boys had found a way in and been daring one another to climb the rusty rungs inside the chimneys up towards the sky. And anyway, cracks had appeared and Borough Surveyor Prescott said they were dangerous.

Richard Torbock's solicitors protested. It had only been last year that the Henley Estate had gone to the expense of getting a qualified architect to report on the chimneys That report said 'they both appear very sound and upright'. The council was undeterred: the cement works chimneys were dangerous and would have to go.

Lyme's assisted wiring scheme and reduced prices had, as the Electricity Commissioners had predicted, increased demand. By April 1934 Arthur Brown reported a 21 per cent increase in current sold compared with the year before. The council cut the price further, to 8 1/2d for lighting and 2 1/4d for power. In a spirit of optimism it raised Les Sharley's wages from £2 to £2 10s.0d a week, granted Apprentice Stan Stocker an extra week's holiday so that he could attend scout camp that July, and even granted Arthur Brown's request for sick pay for an unnamed member of the Department's staff because he was ill.

In June, under the heading 'Lost Lavatory Pennies', a letter was read from a visitor complaining that the ladies' lavatory attendant should have some means of opening the doors when pennies jammed in the slots. No action was taken, but when in August Mrs Toms put in a request for a wage rise from 30s. to 35s. a week, the council responded 'that they cannot see their way to granting her request'.

In the big picture, 1934 saw simple electric fires on sale for as little as 10s., and the introduction of the coiled-filament lamp with 20 per cent improved efficiency. The electric iron was the best selling electrical appliance in Britain. These were often connected to an adaptor in the kitchen light socket and cost from five to fifteen shillings for a non-thermostatic model. The price of vacuum cleaners had fallen from over £20 to less than £10 in the last few years, but the market was limited by the fact that many families could not afford carpets, let alone the means to clean them.

More and more of Dorset was connecting to the national grid. The 60-foot pylons had started their march westwards from Poole towards Axminster in 1932. Now Dorchester, mid-way, was preparing to connect, changing over from its DC system to the AC national standard. Lyme Regis, however, was informed that for the present it would not be economically feasible to include it so, ironically, the first town in Dorset with electricity would be almost the last to connect to the grid. Lyme was to maintain its own eccentric supply for another 15 years.

This did have advantages. When in February 1934 the *Bridport News* carried a story, 'Dorset Towns in Darkness. Grid Electrical Supply Failure', Lyme's lights stayed on.

Modern super-grid power lines from Bridport to Axminster, still bypassing Lyme.

In neighbouring Bridport, the borough council had opened an electricity showroom. People still needed to be persuaded of the benefits of electricity. It was not yet taken for granted; it had to be actively sold. Showrooms offered consumers a chance first to see, then to hire and try out equipment before buying it. Refrigerators and washing machines were still some years off, but electric water and room heating and cooking were there to be promoted. Bridport Electricity Department regularly advertised its showroom in the *Bridport News*:

Electric Cookers may be hired for 3/6d per quarter

Healthy cooking means healthy cooks

Recent striking reductions in charges

No intelligent person can afford
to ignore the advantages offered

Lighting, Cooking, Room-heating, Water-heating and Power

Electricity Supply is a Public Service for the Service of the Public

In Lyme Regis, the Marder Almshouses had been among the first homes in town to be connected to electricity. In October 1934 surprisingly, the occupant of Number 6 applied to join the assisted wiring scheme, suggesting that the original 1910 wiring was now so out of date it needed to be replaced.

Whether the occupant of number 6 was 'an ancient sea-farer of good character' – Captain Marder's original stipulation – is not recorded   All we know from council minutes is that his wife and son 'looked after him to the best of their ability'. One of his neighbours, however, clearly did not look after herself and was given notice to quit her almshouse 'for her habitual disregard for cleanliness'. She obviously dug in her heels because the following June, the council resolved 'so that the occupant be removed, an order for her ejection is obtained'. This must have worked as a further note refers to redecoration of the house prior to its re-letting.

For the year ended 31st March 1934 the electricity undertaking had made a net profit of £123 15s.5d. Sixty-one more premises were connected to the mains, bringing the total to 458, despite 35 consumers being lost when the South Somerset & District Electricity Company took over the supply to Uplyme.   A Mr Leeming was given permission to flood-light the outside of the *Stile House Private Hotel* and pay for current at the power rate; the storage batteries in the Malthouse were reconditioned at a cost of £738, and the Wallis Trust raised no objection to the privately-owned Ozone Terrace being supplied with a light where last summer a visitor had fallen on 'really a most dangerous footway on a dark night'.

In December 1934 the council's Highways Committee debated the novel notion of 'All night public lighting'. Up to then, the town had plunged itself into darkness (apart from the glories of the star-lit night sky) at 11pm when all 135 street lamps were switched off. Councillors quickly rejected the idea as too extravagant, but they did consider keeping eight lamps on until midnight. After further debate this figure was whittled down to five: the three lamps considered not worth keeping alight were the one near the Cobb, one in front of the cottage hospital and the one in front of the police station. If the police wanted a light on outside their police station until midnight, then Dorset Constabulary, not the ratepayers of Lyme Regis, would jolly well have to pay for it.

THIRTY SOMETHING

By 1935, Britain was struggling out of the Depression and 50 per cent of homes were now wired for an alarming array of electricities, supplied by some 625 different electricity companies. There were other things to worry about, too. In Germany, Hitler and the Nazis were busy re-arming and eliminating their opposition In Italy, Mussolini was planning to invade Abyssinia. In London, the Prince of Wales was said to be seeing rather a lot of a thirties-something American divorcee called Wallis Simpson. And in Dorset the County Police Authority had finally caved in after a 13-year debate and appointed its first woman police constable. In Lyme Regis from January, Alban Woodroffe's son Rex was chairing a monthly political discussion group. Britain, unlike Germany, still tolerated political debate.

The British Union of Fascists held their first rally in Dorset on 28th January, in Dorchester. 'Men and women members of the Union marched through the thoroughfares of the town clad in their Blackshirt uniforms and carrying banners,' reported the *Bridport News*. Afterwards, William Joyce* from the London headquarters told the crowd what the Party's agricultural policies would mean to local farmers, and warned of the evils of foreign food. The Union later moved on to hold a meeting at the Drill Hall in Lyme Regis where, reportedly, one father loudly ordered his teenage son to 'get off that stage and stop being silly'.

After 22 years of navigating the borough council through peace and war, Town Clerk Harold Ramsbotham was finally stepping down. He would, however, continue as Clerk to the Justices at the Petty Sessions, held before the mayor every Wednesday at 11am in the Guildhall. In 1935 the bench consisted of Mayor Worth, Alderman Baker, Alban Woodroffe and the town's first woman magistrate, Mrs Coombe.

The council chamber and former courtroom in the Guaildhall today.

* The same William Joyce who in the Second World War rose to fame as 'Lord Haw Haw' broadcasting Nazi propaganda from Germany. In January 1946 in Wandsworth Prison he was hanged for treason.

They were cracking down on begging and illegal parking. Councillor Wiscombe told colleagues 'begging was becoming far too prevalent'. In the summer a 'roadster' called John Taylor was arrested for, rather unwisely, trying to beg from a policeman in Coombe Street and was sentenced to 14 days' hard labour. Irene Foster from Middlesex, who considered the parking arrangements in Lyme 'slipshod', was fined 5s. after P.C. Clapp measured her car protruding 4ft 3ins (1.3m) over the white line into Broad Street from the new car park. Christopher Evans from Essex was charged 7s.6d for leaving his car in what Mayor Worth judged 'a dangerous position', and Stanley Savery of Bristol was fined 15s. for leaving a motor car standing at the top of Cobb Road 'for an unreasonable length of time'. Superintendent Beck had been checking up on Savery and told the bench he had been fined for a similar offence in Bristol the previous August.

Former mayor Sam Harris had died. He was the Broad Street butcher who, back in 1909, had switched the golden switch which turned the town's electric lights on for the first time. The council passed a vote of sympathy for his relatives. In April his estate was auctioned. At the 1909 inauguration ceremony Mayor Harris had jokingly excused his failure to invest in the Electric Light & Power Company with, 'But I am a poor man'. The crowd had laughed. In 1923 he moved from living above the shop to Colway Manor which, along with his farm and two cottages, was now up for sale.

Sam Harris's Colway Manor.

In March 1935 the council agreed to build a new fire station next to the former grammar school buildings on Hill Road, renamed the Woodmead Halls. Mayor George Worth estimated it would cost about £250 to put up a building with a corrugated asbestos roof, 'large enough to keep the fire escape [the ladder] attached to the engine'. And, he reassured councillors, even when it was cold 'the fire engine will be able to get out of the station quickly because the run-out will be on a downward slope'. The old 1921 Dennis engine had no self-starter so the brigade had to crank or bump-start it into life before leaping aboard.

Twenty-five years and the Great War now separated King George V from his coronation and in March the council set up a Silver Jubilee Committee to start planning for the celebrations in May.

Eventually they agreed that the day would begin with Walter Abbott, the thrice-national champion town crier, announcing the programme around the town while the Guild of St Michael's Bellringers rang out the parish bells. Then at 11.00am there would be a Thanksgiving Assembly and Service in the Langmoor Gardens (Drill Hall if wet), the order of service to be approved by none other than the Archbishop of Canterbury. The town band under local builder and Acting Bandmaster Charlie Hallett would attend and be paid £10 for the entire day, including music for dancing in the evening on the Marine Parade.

There would be 'a luncheon for the Old People, Widows and Cripples of the Borough' (budget £15) served in The Gables, the former cottage hospital opposite the church. In the afternoon there would be sports on the beach for the schoolchildren, with medals for first and second prize-winners. Afterwards, a tea for an estimated 260 children would be provided in the church hall (budget £15) followed by an entertainment in the Drill Hall cinema by kind permission of Mr Hardy. 'All burgesses to decorate the outside of their premises (council to purchase necessary flags, bunting and streamers).' And so that all council employees could join in the celebrations, they were granted an extra day's holiday with full pay.

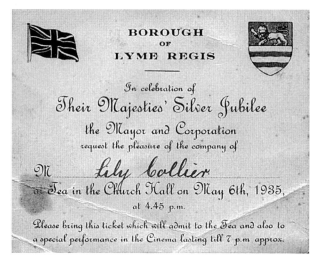

The invitation card sent to all children in town, printed in red and blue.

The Marine Parade would be illuminated until 2.30am by electric lights provided by the Carnival Committee, with free electricity provided by the council. The Langmoor Gardens above would also be illuminated with 'fairy lights', which consisted of hundreds of candles in jars, lit and hung in the trees by the schoolchildren. There would also be a bonfire on the western beach, and a torchlight procession.

As well as free dancing on the Marine Parade, a proper dance would be held at the Woodmead Halls from 10.30pm to 2.00am, admission 1s.6d excluding refreshments. A firework display on the Cobb as a finale was rejected as 'too costly'. Instead a number of tar barrels would be lit along the Cobb's north wall and 'a small quantity of rockets' fired at the same time, to signal the end of the celebrations. The council resolved to take out third-party insurance for the event.

Afterwards Mayor Worth congratulated all those who had helped make the celebrations such a splendid success and Alderman Baker told the *Bridport News* that the Langmoor Gardens presented one of the prettiest sights he had seen in Lyme Regis for many a year.

In May, the council was pleased to learn that the borough electrical engineer had successfully undergone an operation in hospital in London. Assistant Engineer Horace Stone was given a £5 bonus for his extra work during Arthur Brown's absence. Also away, attending a Silver Jubilee Dinner for the Society of Dorset Men in London, was the mayor's senior macebearer and town crier Walter Abbott. He sent his apologies for missing the council's quarterly meeting, the first he had missed since May 1907.

In June the *Bridport News* reported, 'There is much regret at the departure of Mr and Mrs Woodroffe and Mr Rex Woodroffe from Rhode Hill'. It went on to reassure readers that the family was moving only a few hundred yards away to a new house they were building called White Ley. 'Mr Woodroffe will carry on the great work with the Boy Scouts and has very kindly promised the continued use of the bathing pool for swimming instruction. Mr Francillon, having purchased Rhode Hill, has kindly stated that the Uplyme Scout Group can have use of the headquarters, rent free. To this good turn, very hearty thanks are extended, not only by the Group, but by all the residents of the neighbourhood.' Alban was now 60, Mrs Woodroffe was not well and, as he said later, he no longer needed a house with 24 bedrooms. The Francillons established a finishing school for young ladies in the house.

Down by the sea visitor-numbers were steadily rising. The following figures show just how important summer compared with winter was in terms of council receipts.

	Oct to March 1935	April to Sep 1935
Deck-chair hire	10-0d	£157-16-6d
Lavatories	£18-12-3d	£364-3-11d
Cobb Gate car parking	£46-9-6d	£449-0-0d
Bathing & hut sites	£2-10-0d	£1,542-33-5d

Although the Depression was lifting, there was one unwelcome feature of greater prosperity: litter. This was a largely new phenomenon. Nicely brought-up people did not eat in the street where hungry eyes might be watching. That would be bad manners. Most food and drink went straight home in shopping baskets, much of it in brown paper bags or returnable bottles. However, there was a fast-growing market for cigarettes, ice-creams and sweets' and manufacturers were spending more and more on packaging.

In July 1935, the council received a complaint from Lady Pickering about the state of the area near the Cobb. She suggested that the problem might be solved by the erection of a litter basket. This was a novel idea so a sub-committee comprising Councillors Ramage, Camplin and Pitt was appointed and sent off to report on whether any other locations in the town might benefit from these new-fangled litter-bin things. They recommended Lyme Regis to invest in six. And presumably to ensure they were fully used, the council in the same month gave the Corner Shop in Broad Street permission to put up 'an automatic cigarette machine' on the pavement, at a rent of 5s. a year.

In October the council cut the price of electricity for the second time that year, to 7½d for lighting and 13⁄4d for power and gave Mr Geake the dentist permission to light his surgery's operating lamp at the power-rate. It bought 80 second-hand DC electricity meters from nearby Seaton, which was changing over to an AC supply from the national grid, and agreed to provide a light in the newly erected telephone kiosk at the Cobb.

That autumn the council decided to buy an Atco Autoscythe Grass Cutter. Four suppliers provided four identical tenders of £36 10s.0d so the winner was chosen by drawing lots. In November the Reverend G.F.Eyre took over as mayor from George Worth.

The Reverend G. F. Eyre

Stan Stocker finished his five-year apprenticeship at the Electricity Department. Since 1930 his wages had risen every year by five shillings a week. Now a rise of ten shillings brought his weekly wage to £1 15s.0d. The committee instructed Arthur Brown to engage a new apprentice, with the condition that he 'must be a Lyme Regis person'. And the council invested in a new Underwood typewriter for its main office at a cost of £23 8s.6d, the equivalent of Stan Stocker's wages for about three months.

Stan Stocker (right) in August 1936 with cable heading for the Cobb.
The assistant carrying Stan's linesman's climbing-belt is Dick Hitchcock.

In the mid-1930s, 7,000 people were killed every year on Britain's roads, double the figure of today. Bad brakes, tyres and roads contributed as much as bad driving. 'Death and maiming on the roads are now on a battle-field scale,' said the Minister of Transport Leslie Hore-

Belisha*. In Dorset, T.E.Lawrence (of Arabia) and Alfred Laurence of Lyme Regis both died in motorcycle accidents. In Alfred Laurence's case, the coroner put the cause of death down to 'injudicious driving in view of the prevailing conditions'.

According to witnesses, on a late November afternoon in 1935 Alfred Laurence was riding fast along a country lane 'partly flooded and covered by a film of mud'. On a left-hand bend opposite Catheston Dairy he swung out too far and crashed head on into a delivery van driven by George Burgess, out for a pleasure drive with a little girl called Paddy Hunt. Several witnesses later recalled his flaming red hair, so he was not wearing a helmet. Dr Andrews from Lyme Regis arrived. He and Burgess put Laurence in the van and drove to the cottage hospital, but Laurence 'succumbed within a few minutes of his admittance from a compound fracture of the forehead'.

At the inquest the coroner expressed his sympathy to Laurence's mother, 'a tragic figure dressed all in black'. The jury returned a verdict of accidental death, adding a rider that exonerated George Burgess from any blame, and gave their fees to the cottage hospital. That year the hospital got a new wing with eight more public beds and two private wards. Britain got the driving test, the 30mph urban speed limit, the L-plate and the windscreen wiper.

At the start of 1936 Engineer Brown told councillors that demand for electricity in the borough would soon outstrip its generating capacity, and Medical Officer of Health Dr Cook produced his annual report for 1935. In this Dr Cook estimated the town's population at 2,619. There were 37 births (all legitimate) and 43 deaths. Two new cases of tuberculosis had brought the total on the borough register to eight, and there had also been one case of poliomyelitis. However, neither TB nor polio had resulted in deaths.

Over the years two recurring themes in Dr Cook's reports are housing and water. In his report for 1935 he notes that 11 new private and four more council houses in Corporation Terrace had been built. A government-sponsored slum-clearance programme was proceeding slowly. From a survey of about 350 houses in the town, he judged that in 16 homes the families were 'definitely overcrowded'. Twenty-six families had to share their bath tubs and lavatories, a further 21 shared bath tubs, and six more shared lavatories. He blamed one girl's exclusion from school for 'being in a verminous condition' entirely on bad housing.

Overall, Dr Cook judged 17 houses in the town were unfit for human habitation. However the chairman of the housing committee Councillor Owen observed, 'Dr Cook does not have a very free hand in this matter, as it seems futile to condemn places without having alternative accommodation for re-housing the occupiers'. Dr Cook had nevertheless issued two compulsory demolition orders.

The slums to be demolished were known as Jordan Cottages. They stood between the river and the ancient pack-horse track inland, just above where old Jordan Mill now housed the White Rose Steam Laundry. Local landlord Edwin Wallis owned them and the council gave him £40 compensation, but then deducted £13 0s.8d to cover the cost of demolition. The families were re-housed in the four new houses in Corporation Terrace at a rent of 7s. a week, but rent rebates for Mrs Grafton and Mrs Sweetland reducing theirs to 5s.6d and 3s.6d respectively. They were told, however, that in their cases they could only occupy the houses until 'more suitable'– presumably meaning cheaper – accommodation could be found.

In just ten years the council had increased its stock from 20 to 106 houses. The average rent in 1936 was about ten shillings a week, generating £210 of rental income a month for the

---

*Leslie Hore-Belisha, famous for the name he gave to flashing orange beacons at zebra crossings, was a very talented politician but was forced out of office by right-wingers because he was Jewish. Anti-Semitism was not a German monopoly.

council. Yet there were still 52 families on the waiting list for homes. In March the council approved plans drawn up by old Major McDonnell for 28 more dwellings. These would complete Colway Mead, its main council estate, in those days standing separately off to the north of the town. There would be 16 flats, two bungalows and ten 'cottages' with living-room and two or three bedrooms. The council applied to the Ministry of Health to sanction the necessary loan, and the contract worth £8,278 15s.4d eventually went to local builders Eli Emmett & Co.

Chairman Councillor Owen promised that everything would be done to make the new council houses as attractive as possible. But, he explained, 'We have found that very big rents cannot be afforded, and we are trying to get something which will meet the pockets of the people'.

Some of the new houses were intended for families being re-housed from Lyme's slums and he went on, 'It has been put to me that the people who will occupy these houses will not be exactly desirable occupants for Colway Mead. But we have found that if we give a person a better house, they rise to the occasion and keep it beautifully clean. Our almshouses are an astonishing example of this. If there is disgrace attached to the word "slum", surely it is more applicable to the character of the people who own the houses in which the people now reside than to the people who dwell in them.'

Pulman's Weekly added, 'The Reverend Knowles hoped the Council would get on with the scheme and provide houses for people who were living in conditions contrary to the morals, health and dignity of the town.'

Councillor Owen was right: there were tensions on Colway Mead. Just to afford the original rents all the early tenants would have been from better off local families. Now, however, the slum-clearance scheme meant that families from the very poorest parts of town were being re-housed next door to them, families some may well have regarded as 'not exactly desirable occupants for Colway Mead'. The town clerk reported several noisy rows between neighbours and was instructed to threaten them with eviction. Not long afterwards, the Housing Committee wrote to all tenants saying it viewed seriously the growing practice of setting fire to the chimneys of council houses, presumably instead of going to the expense of having them swept. The practice was, the notice warned, probably a criminal offence.

Major Allhusen's home, Pinhay Manor.

Dr Cook's other regular theme was the town's chronic water shortage. For houses on the west side of the town it was to some extent solved in 1933 when Major Allhusen laid on an extra summer supply from his Pinhay estate, provided from the works of the newly formed Lyme Regis Water Supply Co Ltd. Major Allhusen, according to the station master's son at Combpyne, 'was a very nice gentleman. We all used to take our hats off when he passed.'

In 1934 the new company provided the town with 57,000 gallons compared with 46,000 from the town's own reservoirs by the station and at Rhode Barton near Rhode Hill.

During 1935, Dr Cook reported, the town did not need to buy extra water from Pinhay until June, partly because the council had managed to mend some leaky mains and partly because it had introduced a 'free washering of leaky taps' service during the year. By 1936, however, a major leak somewhere in the east of the town was said to be losing as much as 10,000 gallons a day. There were bad-tempered exchanges in the council complaining about the showers provided for visitors on the beach. 'Water comes gushing out of the showers but up in Charmouth Road a tap can be turned on for days without any supply', complained Councillor Pitt. 'Why throw away water on people's heads?' grumbled Alderman Camplin in support.

1935 was the last year for which Dr Cook published a report. He had been producing these illuminating documents since 1923, but from August 1936 Lyme Regis was to join Bridport and Beaminster in a new district health authority. A medical officer of health for the combined district, Doctor MacKay, was appointed at a salary of £800 a year plus £50 travelling expenses. At the end of June, the council gave a vote of thanks to Dr Cook 'for his service to the town and the genial way in which he has always attended to his business as their Medical Officer', and asked him if he would be kind enough to accept one month's notice.

The 1936 Morris 12-4 'Doctor's Coupé' cost £220 new,
including electric windscreen-wipers and self starter.

18

WINDS OF CHANGE

Until the 1930s, council meetings in Lyme Regis seem to have been restrained and respectful affairs. Now there were signs that on some matters two hotly opposing sections had emerged.

One group – let's call them the Modernisers - included Mayor the Reverend Eyre and Alderman George Worth. The other – the Local Champions – included Alderman Camplin, and Councillors Owen and Pitt. The Modernisers were keen to keep abreast with the rest of the country and encourage more visitors. They liked to push things through and get things done. The Champions were financially more cautious, and suspicious of too much power in the hands of colleagues, especially when those colleagues were committee chairmen. The Champions saw themselves as democrats, defending the interests of local families before those of the well-heeled incomers. And as for the summer visitors, the Champions sometimes seemed to regard them as a bit of a nuisance although, as Councillor Owen admitted, two-thirds of the ratepayers in the town depended on visitors for at least some of their income.

One instance of the two sections squaring up was over a proposal to flood-light the harbour. In February 1936 the finance committee recommended putting up two flood- lights on the Cobb warehouse roof. It was hoped their beams would pick out boats and make the harbour 'a great attraction to visitors on a late summer evening'. Engineer Brown estimated that the Electricity Department could do the job for £13 10s.0d for the lamps plus 2½d an hour for the current.

Messrs Camplin, Owen and Pitt tried to get the plan deferred. Councillor Pitt criticised it as 'trimmings'. 'We should spend money only on necessary things. This flood-lighting is for pleasure and we can safely defer it until better financial times.' Alderman Camplin agreed and Councillor Owen said an earlier experimental lamp looked more like some wandering star of Bethlehem. Even car lights would flood-light the harbour better than the light put there by the Committee. But their amendment to defer the plan was defeated.

Another subject for sharp disagreement was the new borough council offices. Until now, the town clerk and other borough officials had used the limited space in the Guildhall, overflowed into the elegant but neglected Philpot Museum next door, or worked from their own offices around town. However, the days of part-time local government officials were numbered and by 1936 the town's administration needed proper offices.

To provide them, the council bought the annexe of the *Royal Lion Hotel* in Broad Street for £3,500 and set about converting the ground floor into offices, the upstairs into flats and finding a tenant for the cellars. The alterations would cost a further £595 2s.6d, plus £70 for Mr James to install electric lights and a power circuit throughout. Repairs to the roof and new furniture and office equipment, including a stapler for the town clerk costing 15 shillings and bought from an Axminster firm ('Why should we go to Axminster? Axminster Council does not come here.') would bring the total up to nearly £4,500.

In April 1936 *Pulman's Weekly* reported a bad-tempered council meeting where the Champions proposed cancelling the project and selling the offices off. At one point Mayor Eyre reminded Councillor Owen that the decision to buy the offices had been almost unanimous and he should just accept it. 'Don't let us have this grudge going on for ten years as in the case of the electricity.' Councillor Owen had led the attempt to sell off the electricity undertaking in 1931. When Alderman Camplin joined in and was told by the mayor to 'Sit down, please: we don't want to hear any more from you', he responded with what looks suspiciously like a sulk. When later on Mayor Eyre put a question to him about his Bathing Committee's report he refused to answer. 'I have been told to sit down. You will have to wait for your answer until next time.' Mayor Eyre said he hoped 'no other member of the Council was going to treat the Mayor with such absence of respect'.

The Reverend G.F.Eyre presiding at a council meeting in the mid-1930s.

Some councillors were concerned about the cost to the ratepayers of the growing number of council employees. In 1936 they resolved, 'As there are already 18 employees permanently employed receiving the benefit of an annual holiday with full wages, and this number shall constitute the Council's permanent staff and be not increased without a resolution of the Council'. However, other councillors were concerned about the unspecified number of labourers and seasonal workers, some virtually permanently employed. They had no guarantee of work, no pension to look forward to and certainly no 'annual holiday with full wages'.

'Nine Years Without Holiday' was the heading in *Pulman's Weekly*. Alderman Emmett told colleagues, some council workmen had been in their employ from five to nine years without having a holiday. He thought they were just as much entitled to annual leave as officials and suggested a week's annual holiday with pay for every workman after 12 months' service. Despite support for his view, the Finance Committee eventually ruled that the idea was too expensive. For the time being the council continued to outsource its labour requirement by hiring men on a casual basis and leaving it up to them to worry about their holidays and pension arrangements.

1936 was an eventful year elsewhere. The Spanish Civil War broke out and Hitler reoccupied the demilitarised Rhineland. In Britain there was the Jarrow March and the first BBC television broadcast. When in January King George V died, Lyme Regis council sent its condolences to the Royal Family, and had the proclamation of Edward VIII's accession read out from the Guildhall steps. Superintendent Carter raised no objection to the 15 licensed premises in Lyme being allowed to stay open late from June to September – an extra half hour until 10.30pm. And Leslie Hore-Belisha, speaking to the St Austell Chamber of Commerce, said that the new reign would see 'the supply of electricity as ubiquitous as that of water', and that it would 'exempt millions of housewives from unnecessary toil, releasing their leisure and their personality'.

In March, the council agreed to erect 11 additional street lamps for £51 2s.6d, and update the wiring at Foreman Boalch's house at the Town Mill for £4 12s.0d. It also agreed to repaint the council's two lorries during slack periods. However, it did not entirely trust Hitler when he said Germany's intentions were entirely peaceful and ordered a further 18 copies of *A Report on Air Raid Precautions* from the clerk at County Hall in Dorchester. It also refused Mr Rattenbury permission to graze his goat on grassland near the cement works.

In April, electricity was extended up Timber Hill to Lyme Regis Golf Club in return for a promise from the club that they would use at least ten guineas worth (£10 10s.0d) of electricity a year for the next ten years. And the council agreed that the fire brigade might attend fires across the Devon border in Uplyme, always providing that they gave preference to Lyme Regis fires. Six silver and bronze long service medals and a Dennis trailer pump and extra length of hose were ordered for the brigade. The latter were needed because the town's low water pressure meant that at one recent incident, 'it had only been possible to throw a jet of water ten feet high'. Now they would be able to pump water directly from the sea for fires at the bottom end of town.

In the same month the Electricity Committee applied to the Urban Committee for permission to install a water turbine 'in the old wheel house' at the Town Mill. The Urban Committee agreed in return for a rent of £2 10s.0d a year. Committees had their budgets to defend.

The private electricity company had used a turbine back in 1909, but that was up river at Higher Mill, and had been sold for £5 when the council took over the company in 1923. The new plan was to install a modern Gilkes 'Francis' turbine at the Town Mill to generate, if you are interested, up to 18.6 kW from a 3.81metre head of water at an estimated flow of 0.62 m³/sec.

The council was investing in this relatively low-output equipment because of the increasing difficulty of supplying the town through the whole night just from its 264-cell battery. However, it was reluctant to run any of three diesel generators in the Malthouse at night, partly because the demand did not justify running even the smallest and partly because of the complaints generated by the noise. A water turbine on the other hand, running across the yard in the Mill, should in theory be able to keep the town going virtually silently from bedtime to breakfast. Perhaps the departure of the Browns from 'Electricity Cottage' also helped bring the noise nuisance into focus.

Electricity Cottage – the Engineer's House at 5a Coombe Street – was built partly over the river and physically joined to the Malthouse. This made the cups rattle and Mrs Brown complain about damp from the river. In 1935 the council had offered to put in a damp-course and redecorate her living room, hall and stairs, but after asking first for a delay on the damp-course work, Arthur announced in early 1936 that the couple had decided to move to a house they had found in View Road. To compensate him for the loss of his rent-free housing, the council gave Arthur a rise of £50 to £284 a year, and the damp-course plan was shelved.

When the question of finding new tenants was raised in council in May, Alderman Camplin said he understood the Browns were leaving because the house was damp. Yet now the corporation was proposing to rent it to another family, still without putting in a damp-course.

The Town Mill of 1936

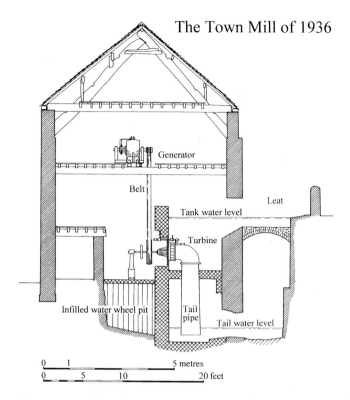

Section of the Town Mill showing the 1936 turbine in a new concrete tank built in the old waterwheel pit. Water from the leat entered over the brick arch, exited below and flowed along a culvert back into the river.

'If it is not fit for one man, it is not fit for another', thundered Alderman Camplin. Deputy Mayor Worth explained that it was not just the damp. There were, to put it delicately, 'home reasons' for the Browns' adjusting their accommodation arrangements. All the evidence points to the 'home reasons' being Mrs Brown finally putting her foot down about the noise and vibration, especially now that Arthur was talking of buying a fourth, even bigger engine for the Malthouse.

In June the Browns moved out of Electricity Cottage, although Arthur kept the Department's office on the ground floor with its separate entrance from the street. The house was let to Charles Hitchcock of 5 George's Court. There were five applications for the tenancy but Mrs Hitchcock had a friend, a teacher at the grammar school, who helped her write to the council making the family's case. She, her husband and two small children were living in a 'two up, two down' cottage with no running water at all. Their nearest tap and lavatory were in a stone wash-house block shared with three other families in the yard. Their rent was five shillings a week and, slightly embarrassingly, their landlord was Deputy Mayor George Worth.

For Electricity Cottage, their rent rose sharply to 12s.6d a week. However, the house was much larger, had just been damp-proofed and redecorated for £136, and had the only bathroom in Coombe Street with hot running water. Mrs Hitchcock let her neighbours use it for 6d a go. On 19th June the Housing Committee agreed to fit a Yale lock to their front door.

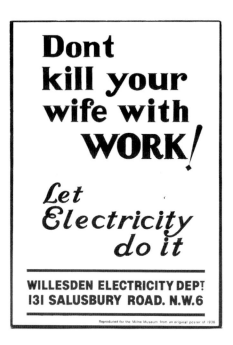

To install the new turbine in the Town Mill, the 'rotten old waterwheel' had to be removed. This was a broad 13-foot (4m) diameter overshot wheel, installed in 1888 by Sampsons of Bridport to power three sets of millstones. From cast iron fragments, it looks as though they smashed the wheel to pieces to get it out. In July 1937 the council authorised Arthur Brown to obtain prices 'for scrap iron and other scrap metal at the generating station', which is probably when the remains of the waterwheel and other milling machinery disappeared.

Across the country, unemployment was falling steadily. The summer figures in 1936 were the best for well over six years. In July 63,000 more people were in work than a month before, and 431,000 more than a year ago. New, slightly more generous dole allowances were introduced. A married couple still only got £1 4s.0d a week to live on, plus between 3s.6d to 4s.6d per school-age child, depending on age. However sons and daughters aged over 18 who lived at home were now allowed to earn £1 a week before their parents' allowance was reduced.

The Advertising Committee distributed 5,500 copies of the town's official guide, and *The Bay Hotel* advertisement boasted: 'Unlicensed. Wash basins (h&c) in bedrooms. Baths. Electric Light'. Visitors could now travel from London to Lyme direct by coach in just under eight and a half hours for 21s.6d return, leaving London at 9.00am and arriving in Lyme at 5.21pm. Down on the north wall of the Cobb, the council took over the diving board and changing huts from the Town Swimming Club because the latter could not afford to maintain them, and charged club members 7s.6d for the season for their use. In *Pulman's Weekly* there were stories about blaring wireless sets causing annoyance to householders, and 51 residents living near the gas works signing a petition calling on the council to do something about the smoke. (Councillor Pitt commented that smoke from the Malthouse was just as bad.)

In August, the national and local press carried headlines such as 'BIG BANGS AT LYME REGIS'. *Pulman's Weekly* reported, 'On Tuesday 11th August, Holiday-makers at Lyme Regis were provided with a spectacular and unusual thrill when two 150 feet chimney stacks and the old cement works to the west of the Cobb were razed to the ground. Three explosions were each followed by the crash of hundreds of tons of masonry, which collapsed on the foreshore near the spot where the Duke of Monmouth landed before the Battle of Sedgemoor 250 years ago.

'The demolition of the chimneys was carried out by the Royal Engineers as part of their army training. The charges were electrically fired by means of a switch behind a barricade. First the buildings on the site went up in a cloud of billowing smoke and soon afterwards the two chimneys were seen to snap near the base and fall full length. Camera men took "shots" of the destruction of the chimneys from behind special sand-bag protections.'

Hundreds of people turned out to watch the demolitions, with the police and fire brigade controlling the crowds and clearing a 'danger zone' around the area. Before each explosion Town Crier Walter Abbott shouted a warning and rang his bell. Mayor the Rev. G.F.Eyre with his wife and General Heywood 'watched the felling of the chimneys from his yacht, *Grey Fox*, which anchored off the Cobb with many other craft'.

Demolition of the cement works August 1936 - photos from *The Daily Sketch*.

The council had bought the 26-acre site in March from the Henley Manor Estate with a loan of £6,500. Having cleared the rubble, it planned to construct a tennis court, a putting green, a car park 'to cope with Lyme's ever-increasing traffic problem'. There would also be, despite vigorous opposition from Councillor Pitt who categorised the plan as 'fancies and fineries', a bowling-green. And people would be allowed to construct beach huts and chalets on parts of the land, at site-rents for day-huts of £2 and chalets £10 per season. For the loss of their allotments on the proposed bowling-green site, Council Foreman Albert Boalch was paid £1 10s.0d and Mr Ridgewell £2 10s.0d compensation

In the autumn, the council agreed to supply electricity to the first twenty six plots of a new private housing development in the Colway Lane Estate. However, Councillor Pitt opposed supplying them with water because he said this would make the water shortage in the rest of the town worse. Councillor Blanchard agreed, adding that he thought 'these people should make their own arrangements'.

In the final quarter of 1936, ten more homes applied to the Electricity Committee to be supplied with current, a further eight asked to be allowed to join the Assisted Wiring Scheme, and 23 existing consumers asked for permission to install separate power circuits and meters so they could use electricity for cooking and heating and pay for it at the lower power rate.

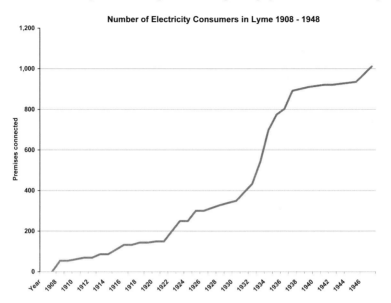

The graph shows the rapid increase in electricity consumer during the 1930s

In December 1936, Edward VIII abdicated over his affair with Wallis Simpson. Lyme Regis Borough Council responded by sending telegrams of sympathy and devotion to his mother Queen Mary, and of 'loyal duty and hearty good wishes' to his startled young brother, the new King George VI. The council stood in silence at the passing of each telegram.

Then despite 'the stormy wind which lashed terrific seas against its historic Cobb', Mayor Eyre wore his robes of office to proclaim the new King's accession around the town. To begin with, his procession included just his two mace-bearers, the deputy mayor, the aldermen and councillors, the town clerk, the treasurer, the finance officer and the harbour master.

The mayor read the proclamation first from the steps of the Guildhall 'after which the crowd sang the first verse of the National Anthem, led by the Lyme Regis Silver Band'. The band and fire brigade then joined the procession, which moved on to the west door of the church where the proclamation was read again. 'Assembled immediately opposite in double file were a few hundred school children who afterwards sang the National Anthem with feeling', continued *Pulman's Weekly*. Finally they all made their way up Broad Street to the steps of the new borough offices. 'At the conclusion of the proceedings the Town Crier (Mr. Abbott) called for three hearty cheers for His Majesty King George VI, and the Mayor called for cheers for Queen Elizabeth.'

In Exeter, 'by the time the Mayor and Sheriff reached the Cathedral, their robes were drenched'. In Bridport, Mayor Palmer, on a raised platform safely out of the rain at the Town Hall 'recited the proclamation in clear resonant tones into a microphone'. Lyme Regis Borough Council did not yet possess a microphone so, if he wanted to make himself heard above the noise of the storm, Mayor Eyre will have had to shout.

TOUGHENING UP

Following the December gales, January 1937 began with some of the worst snowstorms in south west-England in living memory. A French ketch, the Saint Michel, was driven onto the east beach between Lyme and Charmouth. Its crew of four escaped but, according to the *Bridport News* 'Terrific seas hurled her mercilessly against the rocks at the foot of the cliff and she lies almost above the high water mark, with her back broken, masts torn from their sockets and deck smashed to pieces.' 'There's hardly a few pounds-worth of salvage in her', remarked one old fisherman gloomily as he surveyed the wreck.

Mourners followed the funeral cortège of Colonel Thompson through the snow. Typical of one stratum of Lyme society, David Montgomerie Thompson had retired to the town after a life spent defending the Empire and collecting her medals, from Afghanistan to Zululand. At the Siege of Ladysmith in 1899 he won The Ladysmith Clasp. In Lyme he fished and sailed, was a hobby carpenter and regular churchgoer. As well as his widow and daughter, the mourners included General Glasgow, Lady Abbott Anderson, Admiral Eliot, Major Biscoe, Sir George Pickering, Commander Field, and a fellow keen sailor and friend, His Worship the Mayor the Reverend George Eyre.

To most locals, more newsworthy was the death of Alben Wiscombe, former mayor, alderman and chief magistrate, who had died a winter victim of double pneumonia at the age of sixty-seven. With his councillor brother Frank, Alben was partner in the building firm A.&.F Wiscombe and the senior member of an important local family. *Kelly's Directory* for 1935 lists five Wiscombe businesses in the town ranging from estate agent and tobacconist to boot-maker.

Under the heading, 'Loss to Lyme Regis', the *Bridport News* told readers the town had lost a devoted public servant. 'Mr Wiscombe was elected a member of the Town Council before the war, and served for about thirty years. He was one of the advocates of the municipal electricity undertaking, and it was largely as a result of his efforts that the former private company was taken over by the Corporation.' He left a widow, three sons and two daughters. A fourth son, Alban, had been killed in 1917 in Mesopotamia – modern Iraq.

The Electricity Department was getting tough with its consumers. In March when one queried his bill it threatened to cut him off. Another complained that his high consumption was due to faulty wiring and was informed that his wiring was his own affair. By the end of March consumers in arrears owed the Department £50 3s.10d. The Department placed an 'X' against their names in the ledger and warned them that unless they paid at once they would be cut off. And if they paid late in future, their quarterly meters would be replaced with the far less convenient coin-in-the-slot pre-payment meters.

Consumers were also sent a stern warning that anyone caught connecting a light to a power-circuit would be disconnected. It must have been tempting: the cost of current from the lighting-circuit was more than four times the cost for power for exactly the same electricity. All you needed to do was to change the little brown 5-amp plug on your reading lamp to a big brown 15-amp plug and you were away.

However, in those days people were more inclined to do as they were told, and anyway most regarded electricity with some anxiety. Like the ancient Greek god Electron and his wife the goddess Zappata, it was invisible, mysterious and could kill you. The large 15-amp power sockets in your house were fitted with switches which must mean something. So if the council told you not to use the electricity from one sort of socket for another sort of purpose, it would be foolish not to do as you were told.

Later in 1937 a consumer was actually found with a lamp connected to his power-circuit. As punishment he had to pay for all that quarter's electricity at the lighting-rate, was charged an extra £1 fine and had his power-circuit disabled. The council circulated a notice to all electricity consumers telling them that if anyone else got caught trying the same thing they would be taken to court.

By modern standards the corporation's street lighting was still very dim: 100 watts in the main streets and just 60 watts elsewhere. Even in those days their brightness must have attracted criticism as in January the Electricity Committee authorised Arthur Brown to buy 'a special experimental fitting for street lamps at a cost of 29s. to try to improve the public lighting'. Nothing more was heard of this so it can have been no more effective than the experimental silencer fitted to one of the Malthouse engine exhausts that spring in an unsuccessful attempt to reduce the noise.

The batteries at the Malthouse, which stored electricity to run the town quietly during the night, required regular servicing. Concentrated hydrochloric acid for topping them up was delivered to the Town Mill yard in great glass carboys packed in straw. Every year an inspector from the Chloride Electrical Storage Company reported on their condition. In 1937 he proposed relatively modest repairs costing only £179 3s.10d. As usual the Committee accepted.

Electricity consumption was growing fast. For the first quarter of 1937 the committee chairman George Worth reported it up 16.5 per cent on the previous year. The Department's balance sheet looked healthy. The Malthouse roof was leaking so Arthur Brown was told to have it repaired with corrugated iron sheeting and also to have iron extension-pipes bolted to the exhaust chimneys above the roof in another attempt to cut the nuisance from their noise and smoke. Stan Stocker a further got 10s. a week rise and Arthur got new lino laid on his office floor at Electricity Cottage.

Electricity Consumption Growth 1936:1937		
	1936	1937
First quarter - units sold:	81,429	111,412
Premises paying quarterly	493	527
Premises pre-paying through meters	254	275
Total number of premises connected:	747	802
Quarterly meters	898	1,010
Pre-payment meters	256	278
Total number of meters:	1,154	1,288

Total number of premises includes private homes and most of the shops, offices, hotels and other businesses in town. Telephones were also spreading but more slowly. There were just under 200 subscribers in Lyme – one in four electricity consumers was now on the phone. **Total number of meters** More prosperous consumers usually had two meters, one for power and one for lighting, and were allowed to pay quarterly in arrears. Pre-payment coin-in-the-slot meters were usually in the less well-off homes of, for instance, Assisted Wiring Scheme consumers, or in holiday rental properties. These meters cost the consumer 3s.6d to install plus a meter rental charge of 1s.6d per quarter, unless they used more than 10s. worth of current per quarter. Most homes with pre-payment meters only had a single lighting-circuit.

On average six families per quarter were applying for electricity in their homes through the Assisted Wiring Scheme. Each application went before the Electricity Committee for approval. Lilly Collier remembers when electricity arrived in her family's Corporation Terrace home in 1937. She was 14.

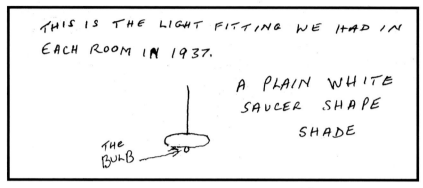

(Illustration by Lilly Collier)

'It was such an upheaval. I can recall when all the floor boards were taken up and how anxious some people were about it all. It was an unknown thing and of course we were not used to it. Before the advent of electricity we only had gas and paraffin lamps, and candles. It was a delight after we got used to the electric lights to be able to switch them on and off in a second.'

Lilly Collier, second from right seated with white socks, with the Brownies in the Rev.Eyre's garden, c.1933.

126

19 TOUGHENING UP

In April, with King George VI's coronation in sight, the council instructed Arthur Brown to buy some coloured lights for the Marine Parade and agreed to provide Mr Harris of *The Bay Hotel* with free electricity for his illuminations. It also ordered commemorative plates and a 'best quality 9ft union jack flag (toggled and roped)' for £1 3s.1d, and a new royal coat of arms to be carved in wood for £16 10s.0d 'as the old one is beyond repair'.

Elsewhere in the town, the council resolved to supply milk to 'necessitous mothers and infants' up to a value of £5 a year, set the charge for the new tennis courts at 2s.6d an hour and bought itself a Morris motor lorry for £343 16s.6d. On the Marine Parade it installed 'a cage and turnstile' at the ladies' lavatory entrance, presumably to replace the attendant, and gave Mr Hodder a £2 reward for information leading to the conviction of two youths for damaging the shelter. However, applications from Mr Phipp of Twickenham for permission to operate a speedboat from the Cobb, and from a Mrs Sanders to run donkeys on the beach were refused.

For the Western Beach, now clear of the cement works, the council appointed a parking and beach attendant at £1 10s.0d a week plus 1½ per cent commission and bought a dozen men's, a dozen ladies' and a dozen juveniles' bathing costumes to hire out from Mr Haddon, the Broad Street outfitter who complained of exploding light bulbs in 1925. On the beach itself it contracted Jack Reid to haul off shingle for 1s.6d a ton, payment to be made to him only after the council had sold it on for 3s. a ton. Off the beach Jim Homyer and his son Victor caught a 9lb lobster measuring 2 feet 7 inches (80 cms), and claimed to a reporter that 500 people had called at their house to look at it.

The need for property-owners to get planning permission for building works on their own houses was still in 1937 a relatively novel idea. The first planning applications on record for Lyme only date from 1923 and, according to Councillor Pitt, 'the by-law had been broken time after time. Whole floors have been added to premises, and sheds galore have been built without the permission of the Council.' But now the council was toughening up.

Charlie Hallett, grammar-school builder and acting bandmaster, was an independent-minded man, more inclined to stop his car where and when he wanted to than go to the trouble of parking it. In the 1920s he had built parts of Corporation Terrace, Colway Mead and, he claimed, Sydney Harbour Bridge. At the end of 1934, a tragic fire at his Harbour Café by the

Cobb had killed his wife when she apparently re-entered the burning building to rescue her dog. Now he was rebuilding.

In the autumn of 1936 the council had written to Charlie reminding him he must submit plans of the alterations he was carrying out at the Café . He needed several reminders. Then in spring 1937 it ordered him to change the colours of the Café's eastern wall, and the fence along its boundary which he had chosen to paint green. At the end of the summer it wrote yet again, this time telling him to stop selling ice creams from the Café on the beach. As with its electricity consumers, the council was clearly standing no nonsense from Mr C.Hallett.

George VI was crowned King of Great Britain, Ireland and the Dominions Beyond the Seas on 12th May 1937. In Lyme the day began with the British Legion, Sea Scouts and other local organisations parading through the town to the Langmoor Gardens, headed by the Silver Band. Four local clergymen conducted a united service in the gardens, the Reverend Eyre read the address and gave the blessing, and the crowd sang God Save the King.

Then, according to *The Bridport News* the streets of Lyme Regis fell silent. For the first time the BBC was broadcasting the coronation service live from Westminster Abbey and the council had arranged the day's celebrations to allow the population to gather round their wireless sets and listen in at home. Later there was a lunch for a hundred elderly residents in the Woodmead Halls, and sports for the children on the beach followed by a tea in the Church Hall.

George VI and his family: coronation plate detail.

After presenting each child with a coronation plate, Mayor George and Mrs Eyre made their way to the west side of the Cobb for the official opening of the new bowling green. The full-size regulation green had 'been laid by experts with the finest Northumberland turf to provide a perfect surface at a cost of £1,100', reported the paper. For coronation night celebrations, the council provided free electricity for all 'approved illuminations'.

That summer, Engineer Arthur Brown was authorised to settle a claim by Mrs Lutyens for three tea cups which the electricity meter-reader had broken during his visit. These regular visits by a council employee to people's homes must have been one way of keeping a fatherly eye on whether they were connecting lights to their power-circuits. It may also have reminded them of the importance of getting planning permission from the council.

The second-hand 100 kW Petters generating set from Totnes. An apprentice would be lowered by hoist into each of its twin 22" (550mm) diameter cylinders to decarbonise it. To the left is one of the 75kW 4-cylinder Marshall engines.

Mrs Brown had been right: Arthur was planning to buy a new generator for the Malthouse. Apart from the newly installed turbine in the Mill, the town's capacity had remained unchanged at 200 kWs since 1925 and more was now urgently needed. In the spring the council obtained approval from the Electricity Commissioners for an increase.

In June Arthur and George Worth, chairman of the Electricity Committee and owner of the only private fridge in Lyme Regis, took a trip to Totnes to inspect a 100kW generator they had for sale. More and more towns were converting to the national grid and so for anyone wanting second-hand DC equipment it was a buyer's market. Arthur and George returned to Lyme having bought the massive set for an all-in price of £345 including dismantling and transport.

In July the first evidence appears that car-ownership was beginning to spread to council house tenants. The council sent round a notice to all the residents of Corporation Terrace and Colway Mead warning them that 'cars must not be parked or left so as to cause an obstruction'. 1937 was the year when speedometers and windscreens made of safety glass became compulsory, and the 999 emergency service was introduced.

At the end of that summer, the Bathing Committee produced an inventory of its stock. The borough possessed 623 deck-chairs, 104 bathing costumes and a large number of tickets. These were for hiring out deck-chairs at 2d per morning or afternoon session, charging adults 6d and children 3d to bathe in the sea, and permitting cars to park for up to a day in a choice of three car parks for 6d. The town's net profit from its beaches reached a peak in 1937 of £1,711 3s.5d. In 1938 it was down £100 to £1,605 and in 1939 a further £50 to £1,552. Whether this decline was due to bad weather, fears of looming war or the disappearance of Charlie Hallett's ice-creams from the beach is not entirely clear.

The bowling green with the Cobb beyond today.

DRUMS OF WAR

As 1937 drew to a close, Hitler was re-arming in Germany and Mussolini was conquering Abyssinia and helping Franco wage civil war in Spain. Britain, under Prime Minister Neville Chamberlain, clung on to its policy of appeasement but began some desultory preparations for war.

Beyond the Cobb on the ruins of the old cement works, the Air Ministry asked Lyme Regis Council for permission to build a boat house and quarters for RAF personnel. It planned to establish a Marine Craft Base which would house fast motor-launches for air-sea rescue operations in Lyme Bay, and provide support for any experimental flights over the sea and bombing practice. In the autumn the council gave consent for the erection of a 90ft by 110ft (27m x 32m) building on a 21-year lease for a rent from the Ministry of £150 a year.

It was domestic buildings, however, that were the council's main concern. It had identified about a dozen houses as slums that it wanted to demolish at the top of the old town on Silver Street, and a clutch more down by the river at Mill Green. At the end of the summer it applied to the Ministry of Health for slum clearance orders.

The orders were for 'the major displacement of persons of the working classes under Section 25 of the Housing Act (1936) from dwellings unfit for human habitation, or dangerous or injurious to the health of the inhabitants, within such a period as may be deemed reasonable.' In December 1937 the Ministry made the clearance orders, but then early in 1938 for some

On the Marine Parade in the late 1930s, one simply had to wear a hat.

reason rescinded most of those made on the Silver Street properties. Perhaps, after years of neglecting them, the landlords had been suddenly overcome by an urge to carry out improvements.

This was a golden age for film and across Britain cinemas were booming. In Lyme Regis the quality of sound in the old Drill Hall was no longer up to the competition in Axminster, so Mr Hardy had a new cinema purpose built at the top of Broad Street next to the Langmoor Gardens. The Lyme Regis Regent incorporated all that was best in contemporary cinema design including double seats in the back row of the stalls. On 11th October 1937 it opened showing a now-forgotten British thriller, *The Limping Man*. Admission was 2s. or 1s.6d for adults and 1s.3d, 9d or 6d for children. (Interestingly, cinemas in Dorset were not allowed to open on Sundays until the following year when the County Council first permitted them to do so. Lyme Regis Borough Council responded to this by passing a motion of regret.)

At the end of the year the council gave Mrs Tahordin permission to graze two goats on top of the Western Cliff, with wonderful views across Lyme Bay to Portland Bill, for 5s. a quarter on condition that she tethered them securely. At the same time Council Foreman Albert Boalch at the Town Mill put in a claim for £1 10s.0d compensation from the Electricity Department for cleaning up the Mill House after the mill leat overflowed.

The flood was due to the newly installed turbine. In the past, storm-water would have rushed down the mill leat, spilled over the waterwheel and returned to the river. Now, if the entrance into the turbine's concrete tank got choked with branches ('and dead dogs and chickens and that'), the leat overflowed and flooded down the footpath beside the Mill, round into Mill Lane, under the Boalch family's' front door and down two steps to flood their floor.

The council paid up and instructed Borough Surveyor Prescott to investigate. He failed to solve the problem as exactly the same thing happened in January 1939. That time the claim included cleaning Mrs Boalch's carpets so from then on, when flooding threatened at night, the Electricity Department posted an apprentice at 6d an hour to stand with a storm lantern by the leat to keep the turbine entrance clear.

In fact the new turbine was rather a disappointment. Sometimes in the summer there was too little water in the Lym to run it at all. Then when it was working, for most of the time it generated just four or five kilowatts instead of the expected fifteen. Only after heavy rain did it run at full speed, but with it came the risk of flooding out the Boalchs' house again.

At the start of 1938, the council applied for an order from the County Court in Axminster to take possession of part of the garden next to the Malthouse. This belonged to number 5 Coombe Street, which the Stoodleys still rented from the council. The council wanted to construct a large concrete silencing pit underneath the garden to quieten the newly installed 100kw Petters generating set. However, when they had asked Mr Stoodley if he minded them digging up his garden, he said he did.

The council obtained its order and proceeded to build its pit. It did little good: in May 'a petition was received signed by residents of the Coombe Street district complaining of the noise etc from the electricity works and the new engine installed therein'. The council resolved to instruct Engineer Brown to 'do his very best to reduce noise and vibration' at the generating station.

The final 28 homes on the Colway Mead estate were ready in January and the council set the rents at 11s. a week for the bungalows, 10s. for the houses and 8s.6d for the flats. At the same time it gave the new Lyme Regis Bowling Club permission to use the borough's coat of arms in its club house for 5s. a year, and resolved to scrap the council's first and now ancient Garner lorry 'in view of its having completely broken down'. This decision was then amended from scrapping to part-exchanging it for a new lorry and finally, despite protests from councillors Camplin and Pitt, to keeping it for ARP purposes and spending money on having it repaired.

Lyme's arms representing the royal lion (for 'Regis') and the sea, as adopted by the Bowling Club.

Air Raid Precautions were already on the national agenda in 1938. Cinema newsreels had shown the total destruction of Guernica by the German air-force during the Spanish Civil War the year before. In Lyme an ARP Committee was set up in January with Mayor George Worth, Councillor Griffin, the Captain of the Fire Brigade and representatives from a range of local organisations, from the Women's Institute to the Boy Scouts. The sum of £2 2s.0d was paid to the Chief Constable for a course of seven lectures in Anti-Gas Training, given to firemen, special constables and other volunteers. In June it was agreed that the newly appointed ARP wardens should go round from house to house to ascertain the number and sizes of gas masks the borough required. In February 1939, 'in view of the great amount of worked involved in the Air Raid Precautions Scheme', Miss K.A.White's salary in the Town Clerk's office was increased to £1 10s.0d a week.

By the start of 1939, fluorescent strip-lighting, the BBC Home Service and the Goblin Teasmade bedside tea-maker had appeared in Britain. There were two million cars on the roads and 67 per cent of homes now had electricity. In America regular TV broadcasts began. In Lyme Regis nearly 890 premises were connected to electricity compared with 350 in 1930, and the council used an Edwardian law to order five hotels and a garage to remove their advertising hoardings from roadsides around the borough.

In March the Air Raid Precautions Committee considered a list of basements and cellars for use as air-raid shelters, but Arthur Brown's proposal to build a reinforced concrete shelter under the Stoodleys' garden to house a fuel-oil tank for the Malthouse was rejected. The fire engine was converted from solid to pneumatic tyres, a large Chevrolet car was obtained to tow the trailer pump around town, and the Home Office announced it would be sending a further trailer pump to Lyme 'for Auxiliary Fire Brigade Purposes'.

By May, 45 volunteer ARP wardens had been approved by the Ministry of Labour, and the council sent a list of vehicles for fire brigade and ARP service to the County Ambulance Transport Officer. He took it upon himself to cross the 1925 Garner lorry off the list and substitute the words 'One Required'.

To prepare for the expected flood of evacuees from the cities, an Evacuation Sub-committee was set up, with Sir George Pickering designated Chief Billeting Officer for the borough.

A letter from the Ministry of Health informed the council that a total of 1,600 evacuee children would arrive in the West Dorset area by train, and that of these 700 would be allotted to Lyme. The council agreed that Mayor Emmett should send a personal letter of thanks to all householders who agreed to foster unaccompanied children.

At the end of May an electric air-raid siren was installed behind the police station on Hill Road, and Mr Robertson was appointed Chief Air Raid Warden. His team of 18 assistants included Sir George Pickering, Major Biscoe and Major Pinney.

Although the town did not yet have an ambulance, a list of 12 official Ambulance Drivers and Attendants including Lady Pickering and Mrs Biscoe was sent to the County Ambulance Transport Officer together with a list of '4/5 seat cars for sitting cases' and the names of three Emergency Private Car Drivers. In August, the £80 profit from the National Town Criers Contest held in the Langmoor Gardens 'was placed towards the fund for the provision of a motor ambulance for the town'.

Photograph courtesy of the Imperial War Museum, London.

Preparing to clean out a teenager's bedroom.

To deal with gas attacks, a Decontamination Squad of seven was set up, with a concrete shelter built in the yard of the Town Mill for £444 10s.0d by Albert Case. Other emergency groups preparing for when Hitler attacked Lyme Regis included a Road Repair Gang of seven led by Council Foreman Albert Boalch, and a Light Rescue Party, also of seven. Brigadier General Swabey directed the Report Centre & Communications Group and Mr Hill the scoutmaster commanded the Messengers. To round off the town's civil defence preparations, the list included three Hospital Supply Workers and seven Miscellaneous Ladies.

Otherwise, life in Lyme continued relatively normally. The relentless rise in demand for electricity meant the council now often needed to run all four generators in the Malthouse at the same time. In June, Arthur Brown and George Worth went to Tiverton to inspect a massive 245kW generator for sale there. However, they eventually decided instead to employ

Taunton council's electrical engineer Mr Turner to review Lyme's entire system. Perhaps the time had come to join the national grid. Meanwhile, they increased Assistant Engineer Les Sharley's wages by 5s. to £3 a week.

Wage-rates in 1939 were becoming an issue. The Depression was over and as the spectre of unemployment receded the trades unions were getting stronger. The borough council paid its workers at local rather than national rates and, as in the case of Les Sharley, pay was often the result of individual bargains struck between the council and the employee. From the unions' point of view, even less satisfactory was the council's practice of sometimes advertising its seasonal workers' posts as 'applicants to state wages'. This pressured the person who most wanted the job into quoting an absolute minimum figure to secure it. Now, however, the unions were seeking for jobs to be graded, and for employees to be paid on a scale according to the grade of that job.

In the summer of 1939 Councillor Blanchard told the council to 'disabuse itself of its rampant antagonism to Trade Unionism'. He alleged, according the *Bridport News*, that 'the question of grading the Council's employees has been shelved or conveniently forgotten' and moved an interview be granted to the secretary of the Transport and General Workers' Union.

Councillor Robertson added, 'It is most objectionable for a man of any conscience always to have to come and hold his hand out for an increase in wages'. He himself stood up for the working man because he had been a working man before he became a director. Blanchard and Robertson swayed the meeting and they agreed to invite the General Secretary of the TGWU to Lyme for talks. But the meeting also resolved that the question of an increase in council employees' wages be left in the hands of the Finance & General Purposes Committee.

Elsewhere, the need for a mortuary for the town had finally been addressed. In the past the cottage hospital had provided space but was unable to offer a permanent facility. Because of the lack of refrigeration, a proposal to site it underneath the council chamber at the Guildhall had apparently been resisted 'by a member whose nasal powers were well developed'. For the same reason, a plan to build one near the Woodmead Halls was also 'vigorously opposed'. Finally, in July 1939 a mortuary was completed in the former sexton's cottage up at the cemetery, and to furnish it the council bought a stained deal table and six bentwood chairs for £2 17s.0d. However, a proposal to provide a portable shelter to protect the cemetery gravediggers from the elements now they had lost the cottage was considered but deferred.

In August, the Emergency Powers (Defence) Act was rushed through Parliament. It gave the government sweeping powers over land, transport and public safety. These included powers to requisition property, billet troops, take control of roads and railways, evacuate children and issue civilians with gas masks. Punishments for breaking the regulations included up to five years' penal servitude.

In Lyme Regis Victor Homyer, the boatman son of champion lobster fisherman Jim Homyer, was convicted of assaulting Alfred Holman on the Cobb. Holman, a clerk and part-time boatman, had been touting for Homyer's boating customers so Homyer had punched him. 'The case attracted great local interest' and a full bench of the borough justices – Mayor Emmett, Aldermen Baker and Worth, Lady Pickering, Mrs Coombe, and Alban and Rex Woodroffe – fined Victor 10s. and bound his father over for 12 months on a surety of £5 to ensure Victor kept the peace.

There were reports of boys damaging the trees planted in the Colway Mead estate. Surveyor Prescott was instructed to erect a notice warning them that 'Persons found damaging trees will be prosecuted'. Boys had also been playing in the Corporation Depot so he put up a notice there, too: 'All persons found trespassing will be prosecuted'. That told them.

But ten German boys on a visit to Dorset in August with their teacher were entertained to tea in the Guildhall. They were welcomed by Mayor Emmett, Alderman Baker, Town Clerk Atterbury and Walter Abbott, the champion town crier. The history of Lyme Regis was explained to them and, *Pulmans News* reported, after tea 'they were interested to hear one of the Town Crier's famous cries'. To round off the afternoon's excitement Dr Lancaster conducted the boys around the Philpot Museum.

Any lingering doubts Hitler had about the wisdom of waging war on England were dispelled when at the end of August 'the boys' reported back to him. On 1st September he launched his attack on Poland.

WARTIME WORKS

F rom Garckes Manual 1938: *Borough of Lyme Regis Electricity Undertaking. Plant: one 50 kW, two 75kW, one 100kW, one 15kW water turbine. Capacity 315kW, with 264-cell battery. 900 (approx) consumers. Prices: power and domestic current 11/2d per kWH, lighting 7d per kWH. Chairman of the Electricity Committee: Alderman G.H.Worth JP. Borough Electrical Engineer A.E.Brown AMIEE.*

By the time war finally broke out the nation was braced for a firestorm of bombing. The declaration was broadcast at eleven o'clock in the morning of Sunday 3rd September. Half an hour later air-raid sirens wailed out over the capital for the first time and, the *Bridport News* told readers, 'Within two minutes the great circle around the Queen Victoria Memorial outside Buckingham Palace was completely empty. Air-raid wardens and policemen had shepherded the people into the nearest shelters and trenches'. It was a false alarm: Hitler kept Londoners waiting another year for the Blitz.

In Lyme Regis on Home Office orders, 14 men had already been called up for full-time fire-brigade duty on September 1st. Ten more joined them on Monday 4th September. The little town, which until the week before had only a part-time brigade, now had 24 full-time firemen. Within a few weeks, however, 'when the war did not develop on the lines expected' they were all released except for three who were retained to keep the old fire engine and trailer pump clean, shone and ready to roll.

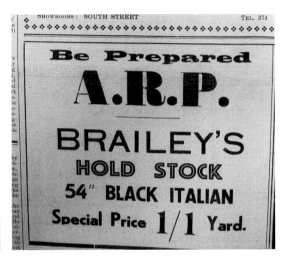

The week before the Second World War began the *Bridport News* carried these advertisements, one above the other, for blackout material to cover windows and this early electric washing machine.

Air-raid warnings were to be given by the new fire-siren the Electricity Department had wired up behind the police station, and another erected along the Marine Parade. If the brigade were required for ordinary fires, Chief Fire Officer Hallett reported he had taken 'the Old Fire Bell which did duty fifty years ago' from the museum and hung it up on the siren tower.

Blackout regulations came into force immediately. All the bulbs from the street lamps were removed and packed away in tea-chests at the Town Mill. Police and ARP wardens patrolled at night and householders faced up to three months in prison and a £100 fine if they let a light be shown. At the end of October, Mayor Emmett chaired a full bench of six magistrates to fine Mrs Shepherd and Mrs Radford ten shillings each for breaking the blackout. Mrs Turner, who failed to turn up, got fined a pound.

In the first few days of September bombing drove an estimated three million people from London and other cities. Many just went away to the country to stay with family or friends, but a Ministry of Health evacuation programme swung into action and trainloads of labelled children flowed out of the capital. Lyme's Evacuation Committee arranged for unaccompanied children to be fostered or stay in two hostels. For evacuees with mothers, they requisitioned a former Anglican theological college and vicarage above the Cobb, Coram Tower and Coram Court, to provide them with shelter and splendid views.

On 23rd September petrol rationing was introduced across the country. The newspapers reported deserted roads in Devon and Dorset and the harbour master reported car-parking receipts at the Cobb down by two-thirds. However, deaths and injuries on Britain's roads soared as a result of the blackout. In December 1939 alone nearly 1,200 people died.

The *Bridport News* 4th February 1940.

At the end of the month, identity cards were introduced and the army arrived in Lyme for training and to defend the coast. For reasons probably more practical than patriotic, the council resolved to allow the soldiers free access to the public lavatories on the Marine Parade, and put up notices outside saying, 'Private - For Troops Only'.

Conscription was introduced and all men in the district aged 20 and 21 were ordered to register for national service on Saturday 25th October. On the same day up in London Rex Woodroffe, now 34, was married to Miss Aileen Allan by the Abbot of Downside at the Church of Our Lady and St Gregory the Great. There was a surge of marriages across the country as, faced with the uncertainty of war, couples hurriedly made or brought forward wedding plans. Most years in Lyme there were only two or three weddings each autumn at the parish church. In 1939 there were seven.

The Bridport News, 20th October 1939.

Censorship was stricter than in the First War. Although the weather from before Christmas to mid-January 1940 was exceptionally cold, with snow and up to 35 degrees of frost, no mention of this appeared in the local press. In early February the *Bridport News* explained to readers that the Censor had forbidden any reference to weather until 15 days after the event 'when the information was no longer of any use to the enemy'. In May there were a few lines in local papers about the German invasion of Holland and Belgium, but nothing on the fall of France or Dunkirk. And the names of those killed or wounded were almost never reported. Men went off to the war. Some came back.

In mid-May, newspapers were restricted to 30 per cent of their pre-war newsprint consumption. For the *Bridport News* that meant its size shrank to a single folded sheet, filled with mainly trivial stories. 'Aliens At Bridport Guesthouse' told of two elderly Austrians. 'Marriage of Mr C.H.Taylor' explained that 'owing to the international situation, it took place quietly on Saturday'. 'Took Toys From Shop' was about an eight-year-old evacuee stealing toys valued at 5s.7d from Dunster's Library in Lyme Regis. 'Hen's Queer Brood' described how amusing it was to watch a hen who had fostered a litter of puppies at Tucking Mill 'preening their fur and attempting to cluck them to a bit of corn'. There was also sensible advice on what not to do with an incendiary bomb and how to escape from a burning building.

At the Malthouse, the Electricity Department staff were exempt from military service as their jobs fell within the Schedule of Reserved Occupations. However one of the three assistant engineers, Charlie Camplin, asked permission to join the RAF. The council decided that 'if Mr Camplin wished to join the RAF, it should permit him to do so', but applied for a Certificate of Exemption for his colleague Stan Stocker and advertised for an apprentice.

At 8.00pm on 4th April the Electricity Committee interviewed four applicants. Chairman George Worth favoured 'Eggy' Loosemore whose father was the town's postmaster. Engineer Arthur Brown wanted Dick Hitchcock whose family had taken over 'Electricity Cottage' at 5a Coombe Street when the Browns moved out in 1936. Dick had grown up playing around the Malthouse and Arthur liked him. In the end they compromised, deciding 'under the present circumstances' to appoint two apprentices. The town clerk wrote instructing the boys to report at the Electricity Department to take up their duties at 9.00am the following Monday. In Dick's case his journey to work was easy: he walked downstairs.

Early in 1939 Dick had left the National School opposite the church as soon as he could when he reached the age of fourteen. At first he had gone to Bournemouth to work in a garage and stay with an aunt. But then war broke out, petrol rationing came in and he was laid off.

Back in Lyme he worked for a while as an errand boy until three jobs were advertised. One was for a projectionist at Mr Hardy's Regent Cinema. The second was for an apprentice telegraph boy at the Post Office, with the lure of a motorbike when you reached seventeen. The third was the apprenticeship at the electricity works. 'I applied for all three, and got all three. I chose the Electricity Department because I'd been playing around the Malthouse for years & knew all the blokes.'

An apprenticeship in those days involved a formal contract or indenture between the apprentice's father or guardian and the master. The master – in Hitchcock and Loosemore's case, Town Clerk Atterbury – took on a number of responsibilities including teaching and instructing his apprentice in that particular trade, and ensuring that he was properly clothed and fed. For his part, the apprentice was bound to the master to serve him faithfully and honestly, keep his secrets, readily obey all his lawful commands, and behave and demean himself as a sober, faithful and honest apprentice. In some cases in Lyme, the master was paid to take on the apprentice, either by his family or a local charity 'for the apprenticing of poor boys in the parish'. In this case, however, the boys would be paid a wage of 5s. a week (plus a war bonus of 2s.6d), and get a rise of 5s. every year throughout their apprenticeships so that at the end of five years they would be earning £1 5s.0d a week. Their indentures would then be returned as proof of their qualified status.

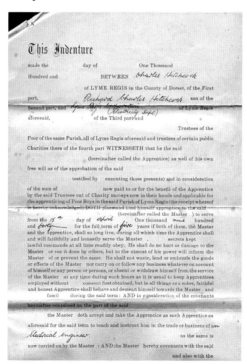

Dick Hitchcock's apprentice indenture with Lyme Regis Corporation.

The Electricity Department the boys joined consisted of the borough electrical engineer Arthur Brown, the chief assistant engineer Horace Stone, Assistant Engineers Camplin, Sharley and Stocker, apprentices Hitchcock and Loosemore, a head labourer Tom Tabberer (the son of Alban Woodroffe's gamekeeper) and two assistant labourers Frank Samson and Turp Sweetland.

The task of the assistant engineers was to man the Malthouse around the clock on three shifts: eight o'clock to five, five to midnight and midnight to eight. On day-shifts they would also repair and service the mains in the town and go round houses reading meters. The labourers had to clean the engines and maintain the works, and fetch and carry around the town. Dick's comment, 'They'd take the ladders off to a job a couple of hours before we'd stroll over to do the work', suggests the difference in status between engineers and labourers, and also the pace and stress involved in the Department's work.

For heavy jobs – digging trenches or putting up a pole – they would take on casual labour from a pool to be found at the Cobb Gate. 'There were always five or six men stood up there waiting to be employed. Some of the blokes were not much good and you needed to be really hard up to pick them. Stoney [Horace Stone] would send me down there. He'd say, "If there's Reg Homyer or Cut Curtis, get them. Tell them we've got a day's work or half a day's work as long as they've got a pick and shovel."' In those days workmen supplied their own tools.

The engine room in the Malthouse showing the smallest generating set. The figure on the left puts the machinery into scale.

At the Malthouse the engineer on shift worked solidly without a break. Every 15 minutes they needed to top up the oil boxes that lubricated the four engines. 'We were using 90 gallons of lubricating oil a week', Dick Hitchcock recalls. There was also fuel oil which had to be hand-pumped from the five storage tanks outside to the gravity tank in the roof above the engines. Every half hour readings from the meters recorded the demand for current, which of the four engines were running and their fuel consumption.

The first peak-demand of the day was at 1pm when people tuned in their wireless sets to hear the news. The old valve sets used as much as 200 watts, the equivalent of four or five light bulbs. At the end of the news the Malthouse dials would show the load drop back until the next news at 6pm and then peak again for the nine o'clock news. With an experienced eye the engineers could also identify from the dials other individual demands for power in the town, for instance the baker turning on his dough-mixer.

The running time of the engines needed to be logged so that after 600 hours each could be stripped down and decarbonised. Before the war, the Department cleaned the tall iron exhaust chimneys by letting them catch fire and burn off: spectacular affairs with flames roaring out of the tops, clouds of black smoke swirling around and pieces of flaming soot raining down on any washing neighbours had forgotten to bring in. Wartime blackout regulations put paid to that. Instead they drilled the tops of the exhaust manifolds and fitted water pipes to spray inside to stop them catching fire. 'So instead of soot you had a black gunge like chewing gum to scrape out,' Dick Hitchcock recalls. 'We couldn't do anything with the damn stuff but dump it on the council tip up on the cliffs.'

Arthur Brown 1871 - 1960 (photographed by his grandson in 1951).

By this time the borough electrical engineer Arthur Brown was almost seventy and walked with a stick. He spent most of his day in the Department's office with its new lino, telephone and electric fire, on the ground floor of his former home 'Electricity Cottage'. There were orders to order, bills to check, wages to pay and customers coming in to settle their accounts. Their cash and that collected from the coin-in-the-slot meters was stored in a drawer in his desk, waiting for someone to wander up with it to Mr Lane, the borough finance officer, at the council offices in Broad Street. For want of a better surface to do it on, the pile of coins was counted out on the floor.

At 9.45 sharp and again at noon, Arthur would make his way to the Malthouse at the back to check log-sheets and get his engineers' reports. Attitudes learned from years serving the Navy and Empire remained with him. His staff wore overalls: Arthur wore a suit. On 1st May each year he marked the arrival of summer by appearing in the Malthouse in a straw hat.

He was a church warden and a strong supporter of the choir. At the same time as his Malthouse men came to the office for their pay, the choir-boys sometimes turned up for weekly pocket-money. On Sundays as a sidesman, he would stand at the back of St Michael's to hand out hymn-books and, allegedly, prod members of the congregation with his stick if they dozed off. But on the way home from divine service, he never failed to buy an extra Sunday newspaper and drop it off for the duty engineer at the Malthouse to read in quiet moments, in the comfort of the deckchair the Department had requisitioned from the Bathing Committee.

Following the fall of France, it was clear that Hitler's next move would be the invasion of England. To confuse the invader, councils in coastal counties removed all the signposts and early in July Churchill ordered seaside towns 'to carry out defensive work to afford protection against a landing of the enemy' and for the mayors of the towns to call for civilian volunteers to help the military build fortifications.

In Lyme Regis the fortifications included a concrete wall, gun emplacements and a pill-box at the Cobb Gate car park facing the sea. Two further gun emplacements were set on the Cobb. Criss-cross angle-iron scaffolding, festooned with barbed wire, was erected all along the seafront and concrete blocks and bent railway rails set by the approach roads to stop tanks. From the end of the summer, unless you had a pass, much of the seafront, the Cobb and the western beach were out of bounds.

Concrete anti-tank defences facing the Cobb, with the Bay Hotel and main town in the distance.

For the Malthouse, the council invested in four steel helmets, four respirators and four pairs of gumboots. The army delivered bundles of explosives and instructions on how to blow up the generators when the Germans landed, and Arthur Brown decided that the safest place to store them was in the cupboard under the stairs.

In late summer skies high over southern England the Battle of Britain was fought and won. People in Lyme would stand on the cliffs and watch the fight. RAF launches from the Marine Craft Base on the cement works site beach were regularly out in Lyme Bay picking up pilots who ditched in the sea. 'I was down the Cobb when they brought in a German pilot that had been shot down out there. There were crowds of people booing and hissing him as he was brought ashore. He spent the night up at the police station and the army fetched him next day and took him away,' Dick Hitchcock remembers.

In September the military authorities requested that an electricity supply be extended along the old coast road to Charmouth, closed off by the 1920s landslips. In the woods above the road the army had put up Nissan huts to serve a searchlight battery. In the field below they had what looked like a farmhouse and hay stacks but in fact were two camouflaged six-inch (150mm) naval guns and a rangefinder. On the golf links at the top of Timber Hill was a naval 'radio detection station' – the earlier name for radar – staffed by Wren.

A splendidly-guarded King George VI visiting the radar station at Lyme Regis Golf Club.

At the Malthouse, Arthur Brown reported that because of the blackout there was a build-up of exhaust-fumes at night. Doors and windows that had always been kept open must now stay shut. The council authorised him to spend £9 10s.0d on an extractor fan and also agreed that during a Red Warning the men on duty should be supplied with refreshments, 'the cost to be borne by the Electricity Undertaking'.

The serious view the army took of blackout regulations was brought home one night when Chief Assistant Engineer Stone and Apprentice Hitchcock got arrested. 'It had gone midnight,' Dick Hitchcock recalls, 'when the shift engineer knocked me up. An underground fault had developed. We had no phones in those days, so I had to go and fetch the foreman from his house in Windsor Terrace. Well, Stoney comes out in his pyjamas with a mac on.

'There was a big fuse box outside the Museum facing the sea where all the main cables were. Stoney with a test lamp was trying to find out which fuses had blown. As he tested each one top and bottom his lamp was going on and off, on and off.

'Then suddenly there was the sound of running and four army blokes came down and arrested us for signalling to the enemy. They took us up to *The Royal Lion* which was where the army HQ was, Stoney still in his pyjamas, and of course all their lights were out, candles stuck in beer bottles.

It took ages, and we never had no identification on us. In the end Stoney said, "You can please yourselves. You can sit here all night in the dark if you like, because you won't get no lights back on until you let us go. So in the end they had to escort us back down to the generating station and the bloke on shift there had to verify who we were.'

Then in autumn 1940 the London Blitz began. During the so-called Phoney War of 1939 and early 1940, many evacuees had been lulled into a false sense of security and drifted back to the cities. Now they, and fear of bombing, returned to Lyme. In the First World War the council had instructed Town Crier Abbott to ring his bell in the event of an air-raid and shout, 'Take cover!' Now they had a clearer idea of what cover meant, and instructed him 'to make a cry asking householders having cellars which would afford shelter to the general public during an air-raid to give their names and addresses to the Borough Surveyor'.

DYING DAYS

Just how many evacuees were sent to Lyme Regis is not recorded, but Sir George Pickering's evacuation committee was busy with a flood from the start of the war. There were Unaccompanied Children, with their labels and little suitcases, fostered with local families or put up in two council hostels. The Gables was the old cottage hospital across the road from the parish church; St Michael's was up above the Alexandra Hotel. Then there were Accompanied Children who came equipped with mothers. Fifty six of these with 25 mothers were billeted in Coram Tower above the Cobb in the autumn of 1939.

However, apart from the Coram children, no further evacuee-numbers are given in council minutes for the first two years of the war. What Hitler might have made of this information is not clear, but when figures did finally appear, in December 1941, they are marked 'Confidential. Not for Publication'. They show 124 children billeted with local families plus 22 more lodged in St Michael's and The Gables. There were also 55 accompanied children and 129 adults lodged with families, and 56 adults and children staying in requisitioned houses: a total of 366 evacuees. A year later the figure had fallen to 182. By spring 1943 it was down to 152.

Back in April 1940 two soldiers appeared in court before Mayor Emmett charged with stealing 'certain sums of money from evacuees at Coram Tower between 10pm and midnight in the night of April 11th'. What the soldiers had been doing in Coram Tower in the first place is not explained, but the evacuees apparently managed to catch one of them because PC Stainer told the court that at about 1.25am he had found a soldier called Rafferty there 'detained by a number of women'. How did they detain him? Did they sit on him?

Advertisement for foster families for evacuees, Bridport News, April 1940.

A few evacuee children may have joined local schools but most seem to have been educated separately in the old grammar school buildings on Hill Road, with their own teachers and headmaster from London. The council ordered two zig-zag trenches to be dug outside in case the Luftwaffe launched an aerial attack on children in Lyme Regis0, and charged London County Council an extra £2 a week to cover the caretaker's overtime.

Although they came with a billeting allowance – 10s.6d a week for five to ten-year-olds, rising to 16s.6d for 17-year-olds and over – evacuees were not universally popular. Some children came from the poorest homes in London. Locals found their speech incomprehensible, their habits alien and their bodies frankly dirty. In October 1941 the Evacuation Committee asked the town clerk to write to Messrs Hoverden asking them to quote for the supply of a pair of electric hair clippers. Presumably some of the children needed their heads shaved because they had lice. Certainly the district medical officer of health judged one caravan occupied by evacuees on the East Cliff unfit for human habitation.

The *Bridport News* reported 'systematic thieving' by evacuee children from shops in Bridport. In the summer of 1941 Lyme Regis Council proposed a blanket curfew for all evacuees. The plan was eventually rejected on the advice of Town Clerk Atterbury, with responsibility for the children's good behaviour being left in the hands of their families' or hostel wardens.

'On the Kitchen Front': as food grew scarcer there was government advice from *The Bridport News* on how to make it stretch.

At the meeting about the curfew, councillors also discussed the cost of feeding the unaccompanied children in the two hostels. At St Michael's, Mrs Graham was spending over 10s. per head per week while at The Gables it was costing only about 5s. The Committee put this down to Mrs Graham not following the government diet sheets 'intended to provide a healthy balanced diet'. Or she may have been cooking more food, better food or just food the children actually liked. In any case she was told to be more careful. To compensate the children for their reduced or less exciting diet, the council voted them an increase in their milk ration from half a pint to a pint a day.

At the St Michael's hostel, wire netting had been erected to protect the flower beds in the conservatory. 'This had not proved a great success', the chairman of the Evacuation Committee reported so instead the Committee ordered that 'two inches [50mms] of concrete be now put over the beds'.

A similar ingenious solution was found for St Michael's electricity supply. Contrary to instructions, this was not being disconnected at the mains at night. The instructions were probably intended to save electricity and also ensure that blackout-regulations were kept, but the result was that the staff as well as children were having to spend their nights in the dark. The staff had instead apparently been removing the children's light bulbs but continuing to use their own. In the end the Committee ordered all the bulbs in the hostel to be replaced, but first had them painted with 'a blue distemper', which means they were painted blue.

The council determined that 'Free bathing would not be allowed to the evacuee school children', but they did introduce a special evacuee bathing rate of 2d instead of 3d for the under-14s, a concession they refused to extend to the members of the local Youth Club. And as Christmas 1941, approached they agreed to hold a party for mothers with children under five, and to invite the older evacuee children, along with the local children they were billeted with, to a cinema show at the Regent, 'courtesy of Mr Hardy'. Also, 'each child be given two new copper coins & buns'.

Relations with the military were generally cordial. In March 1941, Engineer Brown reported that 'two members of the RAF and a fireman, in placing a ladder against a pole to rescue a cat, had damaged an insulator and cut off the supply of electricity to part of the town'. Town Clerk Atterbury was asked to write to Flight Officer Turnbull pointing out the seriousness of this and also the danger in which the men had placed themselves.

At the end of the year, after a dance at the Woodmead Halls, there were 'complaints of the disgraceful state around the fire station [next door], and that in the morning the Fire Brigade had to act as a sanitary squad'. The town clerk and finance officer interviewed the army authorities when next they applied to hire the Woodmead Halls. 'As a result, Military Police are in attendance and behaviour is greatly improved.'

As for the fire brigade itself, it seems to have been deployed at some considerable distances from Lyme, with even a suggestion that it served a spell up to London. In August 1941 it was taken over by the Government and became part of the newly formed National Fire Service. The *ARP Year Book* for 1940/41 shows Lyme's brigade expanded to include the original Dennis fire engine and trailer pump, a second trailer pump, two fire tenders and 760 metres of hose. However, personnel had shrunk back from its 1939 panic peak to 14 retained men and three volunteers. The entry also shows that the town had finally got its own ambulance, 'in service for 2 months'.

The relentless rise in demand for electricity continued despite the war. Any lower consumption by locals because of the blackout and general wartime frugality was more than offset by new demand from the military. In April 1941 the army wrote to the council saying they considered the electricity charges were very high – true compared with the rest of the country – and requesting a reduced rate. The council resolved 'that the military authorities be informed that it is unable to accede to their request, and at the same time asks that the troops exercise economy in the use of electricity as the output of the generating station here is limited'.

They were right. In February 1941 Arthur Brown warned the council it was 'imperative that an additional supply be obtained next winter as during the month of January 1941 the maximum output had been reached'. On January 3rd for about an hour he had had to run all four diesel generators and the water-turbine flat out barely to meet demand.

In fact, the end of independent electricity generation in Lyme Regis was clear for all to see. By now all its neighbours – Axminster, Bridport and Charmouth - were supplied by the national grid, and the arguments for retaining the town's eccentric 440-volt DC system sounded increasingly unconvincing.

These arguments were first that re-wiring the town to take an AC supply from the national grid would be very expensive. True in the short term, but sooner or later the change was inevitable and anyway Lyme's own home-made electricity was far more expensive than the national grid supply.

Secondly, the change might cost local jobs. Yes, but in wartime Britain unemployment was hardly a pressing problem.

Thirdly, it would involve the loss of historic independence, proud local control, and a long and noble tradition of doing things differently from everyone else in Dorset. Think of the Civil War when the rest backed those loser-Royalists while Lyme backed winning Parliament, even if it did get almost burnt down to the ground in the process. How true. How very true.

In response to Arthur's warning, the council arranged a meeting with Consulting Engineer Turner from Taunton, 'with a view to securing a supplementary supply from the Grid'. It also put Plan B into action: raising the price of power from 1½d to 2½d a unit to discourage people from using it; the first time it had increased electricity prices since it took the undertaking over in 1923.

In June 1941 the Electricity Commissioners gave their provisional approval for Lyme to import a bulk AC supply from Bridport. However, the work of erecting the overhead power lines and installing the necessary equipment to convert it from national grid AC into Lyme Regis DC could not possibly be finished by the coming winter. Instead, the council decided to send round a notice printed in red ink asking consumers 'to exercise extreme care in the use of electricity for radiators and power appliances during the months of December and January'. If consumers failed to heed the warning, the Malthouse would overload, break down and everyone would be left in the dark.

That summer, despite his reserved occupation status, Stan Stocker followed Charlie Camplin into the RAF. Then in July a big black car drew up outside the Malthouse and the man in the back with the bowler hat asked where he could find Horace Stone. Chief Assistant Engineer Stone and the official closeted themselves away for a couple of hours. It transpired that the Air Ministry wanted Horace to leave Lyme and work for them electrifying aerodromes.

When Stoney informed the Electricity Committee they were not pleased. Apart from the very real problem of finding a replacement, they had only just given him and Les Sharley a 5s. a week rise. If he wanted to go they supposed they would have to release him, but Mr Stone was informed that 'the Council could not guarantee his re-instatement when his work with the Air Ministry was complete'. That seems to have given him pause for thought because he was still working for the Department in November. But relations had worsened. He seems to have fallen out with Borough Engineer Prescott because a reference appears in council minutes about Mr Stone failing to show due respect, and when his application for a rise to £5 10s.0d a week plus 6s. war bonus was rejected, he gave a week's notice and left.

With Camplin, Stocker and Stone gone off to the war, and Apprentice Loosemore released to enter a government training school, the only pre-war hands at the Malthouse were Arthur Brown and Les Sharley. Two new assistant engineers, George Rice and Rolf Hawker, were engaged at £3 3s.0d a week. However, it took Arthur almost a year to find a replacement for Horace Stone. A boy called Charlie Rice was employed for 10s. a week to read the meters, and Apprentice Hitchcock was now sometimes left to run the generating station on his own.

Rolf Hawker (left) and Dick Hitchcock on the Marine Parade.

The remaining old hand Les Sharley stayed on at the Malthouse throughout the war. His father held a fairly senior position in the Transport and General Workers Union and Les, a union activist, promoted the TGWU not just at the Electricity Department but in other council departments and also in building firms around the town.

So, despite the war, there was a surprising amount of union activity in Lyme. It was not just a question of wages and conditions in the little country town having fallen behind the rest of the country. They had never caught up.

In April 1940 the council agreed that,' the Electricity Committee shall examine the conditions obtaining at the generating station and investigate the cause of the alleged dissatisfaction existing thereat'. It also agreed to review all council salaries and wages, accepted a union proposal that hourly-paid men get an immediate rise of ½d an hour and gave Electricity Department employees 3s. extra a week

In January 1941 at a meeting with the TGWU the council agreed to a 2s. a week increase for all manual employees, and that it would affiliate to the Joint Industrial Council with a view to securing the re-grading of all jobs. As Christmas 1941 approached the union tried but failed to get Tom Tabberer re-graded from Labourer to Linesman, but it did persuade the council to let men leave work at noon on Christmas Eve without loss of pay.

The difficulty of raising Lyme's electricity workers' wages to national levels was that all the national scales were designed for power-station producing at least 1,000 kWs. The Malthouse output was 300 kWs maximum. In larger power stations there were also seven or eight different trades: switch-board attendant, engine driver, battery operator and so on. In Lyme the engineer on duty did everything. Of course the union argued that the Malthouse was just a smaller version of Battersea Power Station, and of course the council resisted. In the end they agreed to pay the lowest rate on the national scales. In early 1943 Les Sharley was re-graded engine driver, George Rice and Rolf Hawker became assistant engine drivers, and they received rises of two or three pounds a week.

Elsewhere, the town had to try to keep going as a seaside resort. In September 1939 the Advertising Committee persuaded the council not to reduce its usual publicity grant for the 1940 season. Visitors (providing they were not German) could still arrive by train, but petrol rationing so reduced the number of cars that, by 1942, car-park attendants could keep 50 per cent of their takings as the only way to make the job worthwhile. The eastern and western beaches were permanently closed off by the army. In the season the main beach was open for bathing during the day, but closed off with barbed wire every night.

The council continued to charge people to swim - 6d for adults and 3d for children - for the three daily bathing shifts: 10am to 1pm, 2pm to 5pm and 5.30 to 9.30pm. There were still deck chairs, bathing costumes and towels to hire, but for the latter you paid a 2s. deposit. As the war progressed, the main beach was closed earlier at 7.00pm. A request from the bathing attendants for 4s.6d a week compensation for the early closing was rejected.

NEWS, FRIDAY MARCH 8, 1940

MINISTRY OF FOOD

MEAT RATIONING
begins
ON MONDAY

On and after Monday, March 11th, the full meat ration will be 1/10d. worth per week, or 11d. for young children with a Child's Ration Book.

There was the national frugality and salvage campaign. The press offered all sorts of advice on how to avoid waste, eat economically and make do. Lyme's allotment holders were urged to join the 'Dig for Victory' campaign and protect their crops from rabbits and marauding members of the crews of nearby anti-aircraft guns. The council provided extra land for cultivation but managed to resist an official request to plough up the sports field above Corporation Terrace. There were collections of scrap metal and paper, with the weights in tons published to encourage greater efforts.

At the end of October 1941 the Ministry of Supply directed the council to conduct a survey and list all the 'iron railings, steel posts, chains, bollards, gates and similar materials' in the district. All this ironwork could then be removed and melted down to make armaments. 'Although compensation will be paid, it is hoped that owners will give freely.'

Owners could apply for exemption. Railings etc would not be taken a) if they should be retained for safety reasons, b) were necessary to prevent cattle etc from straying, and c) had special artistic or historical interest. Owners (including the council) had 14 days to apply for exemption from the date the council's survey was complete. The lists from the survey would be posted on public notice boards but not published - presumably for security reasons - in the local press.

In January 1942 nearly thirty applications for exemptions were accepted. Many were by the council itself, and most were to preserve railings and balconies on safety grounds. But the rest of the public ironwork in town, including the railings outside Electricity Cottage and the entrance gates to the Langmoor Gardens, were cut off and disappeared.

By now all four engines in the Malthouse were showing their age. Each was nursed along, guzzling oil. One had a new crankshaft fitted, another a new piston and liner. At the start of 1942, the Committee had just ordered another cylinder liner for £79 10s.0d when, at about eight o'clock in the evening of Saturday 14th February, all the lights in Lyme went out.

OUT WITH A BANG

That Saturday evening Dick Hitchcock was at the cinema. He can't remember what the film was and anyway never got to see it but, according to the *Bridport News*, on 14th February 14th 1942 the Regent was showing Shaw's comedy *Major Barbara*, starring Wendy Hiller, Rex Harrison and Robert Morley.

The Regent was one of very few buildings in Lyme which still generated its own electricity and was therefore independent of the town's supply. 'I was sitting in the cinema, the film had just started and 'Spike' Hardy the manager came up. "Dick, the electric in town's all gone off". So I went down Sherborne Lane to the town. I could hear the noise from the Malthouse as I was going along the Lynch. When I got there, there were crowds of people outside.'

There had been an explosion. It seems that a great piston-head in one of the 75kW Marshalls had broken loose from its connecting rod and jammed at the top of a cylinder. On the rod's next stroke up the cylinder, it had driven into the lower edge of the piston, smashing off not just the cylinder-head but most of the top of the engine. A great chunk of iron was launched across the Malthouse into the 100kW Petter. 'It wasn't just the top. It was the whole trunk, a piece about twelve foot long, about four or five ton', Dick explained. 'And part of the piston went the other way and stuck in the field winding of the set running the other side of him.'

'The engine didn't stop but he broke all the exhaust pipes off. You see he was still firing on three cylinders, the crank shaft going round with a six foot connecting rod smashing everything to hell. The pipe broke off above the water pump so there was a hundred gallons of (river) water a minute going up in the air from the cooling system, and you couldn't get near in to shut the damn thing off.

'Old Rolf Hawker, he was on shift in there, but you couldn't see anything, just smoke everywhere, flames and that. It was all the oil and that all over the place. The three cylinders had open ports, no exhausts on, belching flames every time they fired. It was horrendous in there and the noise was terrific. I found Rolf up at the control panel. He couldn't turn the engines off so in the end we went up the ladder and punctured the diesel tank in the roof and starved them of fuel. That stopped them.'

Next day, Sunday 15th February, the Electricity Committee held an emergency meeting and inspected the damage. The understated minutes record, 'The Electrical Engineer reported that during the previous evening a serious breakdown had taken place, the result of a piston seizing in one of the 75kW generators. The Armature of the 100kW generator had been damaged, and ...'

Arthur Brown told the Committee that Lyme's generating capacity had been cut from 300 to 50kWs. However, if they disconnected the power circuits in every house, they should be able to generate enough current to restore lighting to the town. The ARP wardens were sent round informing people street by street that their lighting, but only lighting, would soon be on again. They were followed by Electricity Department staff and local electricians who removed the fuses from every power circuit they could find. The wartime censor made sure that not a word ever appeared in the press.

The newspaper billboard that never appeared.

The Committee set about getting the 100kW generator off to the manufacturer for repair. Mayor Emmett said he would try to arrange transport that coming Saturday rather than delay even into the following week and sent a letter of appreciation to Assistant Engineer Hawker for the way he had handled the emergency.

As for the Department's staff, as well as removing the fuses from all the power circuits in town, they had the Malthouse to sort out. Only the original 50kW Marshall had survived unscathed. The two 75kW Marshall sets were identical; the engine of one had shattered and, in the process, written off the generator on the other. 'So we shored the roof up with poles and iron girders, and used the parts of one to repair the other. It took us three days and nights to transfer over all the doings, and at the end of the week the council complained about the amount of overtime we were claiming for.' But within a week they had two sets running again.

At the end of March, the repaired armature from the 100kW Petter returned, was wrongly connected up by the Electricity Department and then correctly connected up by an engineer sent down by the manufacturers. By mid-April 1942 three of the four Malthouse generators were working again, but the town still needed more electricity.

On April 16th the council accepted a tender from the Pirelli General Cable Co to import AC power from the national grid via Bridport. The cost for bringing in a 6,600-volt supply on overhead cables would be £2,845 6s.9d. At the same meeting it agreed to fit an electric alarm bell in Apprentice Hitchcock's bedroom at Electricity Cottage 'in order that he may be called to the Engine Room in an emergency'; and learned that 149 rats had been destroyed at the town dump, 'and possibly many more by gassing'. The Ministry of Food had asked councils across the country to take action as rodents were destroying valuable foodstuffs.

The explosion forced the town to review and speed up its plan to connect to the national grid. That June the council employed a new consulting engineer from Plymouth, Mr C.L.E.Stewart MIEE, to prepare a report on whether to convert just the western part or all of Lyme to AC power from the national grid. On 17th July he presented his report.

The explosion, he said, had reduced the Malthouse capacity to 225kW and 'the position is serious, if not critical. I will state right away that it is no good contemplating putting in further generating plant. The Commissioners would not sanction it.' He went on to recommend keeping the whole town wired for its existing DC system until the war was over. Then, but not until then, would be the time to change to a new 3-phase AC system. In the meantime he proposed bringing the AC bulk supply from Bridport and converting it to DC power to match Lyme's existing home-grown supply using a mysterious piece of equipment, a second-hand motor converter. 'This should be picked up cheaply and could be disposed of as scrap after the change [to AC] is complete, at a figure not far behind what you have paid for it.'

His plan could be carried out with the minimum of delay, and with little material and labour involved. He added that when the war was over there might be a good deal of unemployment, and the changeover to a new AC system 'would be a splendid opportunity for an unemployment scheme'.

Engineer Stewart ended by saying that having gone to the trouble and expense of erecting an eight-mile overhead transmission line, the council should make full use of it. 'A considerable saving can be effected by shutting down your generating plant, and using only the bulk supply.' In a nut-shell his recommendation was that as soon as possible electricity generation in Lyme Regis should come to an end.

In August, an agreement was signed with Bridport Corporation to provide the town with a bulk AC supply and, at the end of September, to convert the AC to DC, the council bought a second-hand motor-converter from Poplar Corporation in East London for £3,000. However, as this had a capacity of only 250kWs and at peak demand Lyme now consumed over 300kWs, the surviving generators in the Malthouse would still be needed.

The motor-converter arrived in a single piece weighing 28 tons. Its installation required the building of a new 10-foot wide bridge across the Lym and, to get it into the Malthouse, a new entrance punched through one of its ancient blue lias walls. The converter was trundled down the Mill Lane on rollers and the council took out insurance cover of £3,000 for each of the workmen involved.

The overhead transmission line from Bridport still had to be completed and it was more than a year after the explosion, on 20th April 1943, that the motor-converter was put 'on load', and Arthur Brown reported that the Department's own generators had been shut down.

In a final letter, Consulting Engineer Stewart explained why the cost of bringing in the bulk supply had over-run his estimate of £4,500 to a final figure of £6,192. As well as higher material and labour costs, progress had been slower than expected. 'In the old days, with Irish navvies at 6d an hour, I reckoned on six yards per man per day; but in this case, as far as I can make out, they have only done ¾ yards per man per day.'

Elsewhere in Lyme, there was trouble with the mains in Broad Street. At first they thought it might be sewage but luckily it turned out to be only water. Anyway, the liquid had seeped into the boxing around the underground cable and caused the paper insulation to decay. The result was a power failure and Mrs Baker of the *Cosy Cafe* claiming £7 3s.3d for the cost of fish damaged when her 'Frigidaire' went off. Mr Lloyd of *The Three Cups Hotel* claimed £6 1s.9d for his loss of fish and milk for the same reason. The council informed both of them that it did not accept liability.

By mid-1943, things were looking brighter for Britain. America had joined the war, Rommel had been defeated in North Africa and the Allies were preparing to invade Italy. On May 17th the Dambusters bombed the Ruhr dams. In Lyme Regis, however, blackout regulations were still strictly enforced, and the owners of *The Three Cups Hotel* and a Mrs Smith of Woodmead Road were both taken to court for letting their chimneys catch fire.

The council's total income for the period April to September 1943 was £13,459 5s.9d. Among other sources it was made up from:

General rates	£5,280
Electricity	£2,779
Council house rents	£1,599
Bathing & chairs	£1,292
Water	£787
Lavatories	£211
Salvage & Waste	£109
Evacuation	£47
Car parking	£2

The contributions from electricity and bathing to the total are striking. So is the tiny receipt, thanks to petrol rationing, from parking.

As the year progressed, there were several anxious references in council minutes to 'the Electricity Trench'. In May, 'A strict watch is to be kept on the Trench'. In September it was noted, 'the Trench is to be filled in and priority supplies of tarmac are to be obtained for this purpose', and later, 'The Electricity Trench is being patched when materials are available'. Although never specified, the trench must have been for laying the final length of cable underground from Bridport to the Malthouse. The anxiety was for people blundering about in the blackout and falling in.

Mayor and Mrs Emmett supporting the 'Lend Your All' national savings campaign.

23 OUT WITH A BANG

In May 1943 the Man-Power Board notified the council that Rolf Hawker's deferment from call-up had expired. It replied that the Electricity Undertaking was scheduled under the Essential Works Order, and wished to retain the services of this employee. The letter must have worked: Rolf stayed on with the Department for the rest of the war.

Apprentice Hitchcock, however, was now 18 and getting restless. 'I was about the last young chap in Lyme. I got fed up going round to houses and people always asking why I hadn't been called up, because all their sons had. As soon as you were 18 you had to go for a medical, and if you passed you got called up within about two weeks.'

Arthur Brown told Dick he could not be spared and, when Dick persisted, Mayor Emmett himself called at the Hitchcock's house to argue the case. However, Dick was adamant and they eventually gave in. Arthur advised him to join the Navy as an electrician, and promised the council would count his time in the service as part of his apprenticeship. At the end of June 'it was reported that R.Hitchcock, Boy Apprentice, had been called up for Military Service, and that it was decided not to fill the vacancy'.

The Department was making a loss so not replacing Dick was an obvious economy. As the plan now was to import 80 per cent of the town's power from the national grid and generate only 20 per cent in Lyme, the pre-explosion staffing level was no longer needed. In September, in a further move to reduce the deficit, the council decided to make Tom Tabberer and the recently arrived new chief assistant engineer Mr Ewart redundant. It also increased the price of lighting to 7¾d a unit. The economy measures worked: for the year to April 1944 the previous year's loss was transformed into a gross profit of £2,893.

L. to R. L. Peters, George Groom,
Clyde Simmons, H. Saylor, Leonard
Wardle, R. Sweeney, Paul Shorter (Stan

American troops in the woods under Timber Hill.

23 OUT WITH A BANG

In the summer of 1943, American troops arrived in Lyme Regis to prepare for the invasion of France. Their camp was in the fields above Corporation Terrace where they put down lorry-loads of shingle from the beaches because their vehicles kept getting bogged down in the mud. 'Most of the people seemed to get on all right with the Yanks. I suppose the girls were having a good time,' remembers one resident. Mayor Emmett and the Amercian Colonel agreed that dances at the Woodmeads Hall should be supervised by military police.

In early 1944 in the run-up to D-Day, the War Department paid the council £5 and compulsorily requisitioned the Children's Playing Field for troops to camp on. It also informed them that Lyme Regis fell within Protected Coastal Area 3. These Areas were designed to increase security along the south coast by restricting civilian movements while the armies prepared to launch themselves across the Channel.

For residents the regulations meant that they could travel about in Dorset but not in Devon. As Devon began just down the road, this was inconvenient, especially for the people across the border in Uplyme who were registered to buy their food rations in Lyme. Town Clerk Atterbury told the council that his interpretation of the regulations was that Uplyme residents must surely still be allowed to come into town to shop.

Even before D-Day, there was a growing mood of optimism and the council was starting to look beyond the war. Housing plans put on hold in 1939 were reactivated. In May the Ministry of Health sent an admission ticket to inspect 'a Factory-made house' in London. Three quarters of a million homes had been destroyed by bombing and there was talk of making 150,000 'pre-fabs' in aircraft factories in the next year. Mayor Emmett took the ticket and Surveyor Prescott applied for a second so they could travel up to town together.

–roll up with your Savings

The *Bridport News*, June 1944, the week after D-Day.

In the autumn it transpired than none of these particular prefabs would now be allocated to Lyme – 'they were intended for blitzed areas' – but by now the council was working on plans for 64 new conventional three-bedroom council houses of its own.

Consulting Electrical Engineer Stewart was asked for advice on their electrical design. He suggested each be wired for a cooker and water-heater, and have four plugs in the kitchen, three in the living room, one in the dining room and two in each bedroom. In case the council considered this extravagant, he assured them that the modern system of wiring a house was much less expensive than in the past. An exhibition of 'Government Erected Post War Houses' had opened in Northolt, so Mayor Emmett and Surveyor Prescott went up to London again, this time taking a member of the Lyme Regis Women's Institute with them.

Although pre-war council housing was usually well built – unemployment in the 1930s squeezed all but the best workmen onto the dole – the planned new post-war housing would leave Corporation Terrace and Colway Mead looking distinctly old-fashioned. Ken Gollop grew up in a Colway Mead house during the war and remembers his family's home well. It was one of the semi-detached 'parlour type' houses begun at the end of the twenties.

'The main door was on the side. Ahead was the front room or parlour which we normally only used on Sundays and special occasions. If you turned left there were the stairs and beyond them, the scullery. The main downstairs room was the kitchen/living room. We only had three electric lights: one in the parlour, one in the kitchen/living room and one in the main bedroom. I can't believe we didn't have a light on the stairs, but I really can't remember one.

'Upstairs there were three bedrooms and the bathroom. There were gas lights in the second bedroom and the bathroom, but we never used them. The hot water in the bathroom came from a gas geyser. We children used to go to bed with candles until about 1946.

'In the main room downstairs there was a coal range, which mother cooked on and which kept the room warm. We kept the coal under the stairs. In the scullery there was a gas copper for heating water for laundry, and a gas ring for a kettle. People didn't have fridges or washing machines until much later. When they finally got them, they put them in where they used to keep the coal under the stairs.'

In November councillors resolved that 'in all future instances where existing council houses fall vacant and they are not wired for electricity, the house be so wired by the Council, and that all gas ring points be taken out of the house'. The 'gas ring' here refers to gas pipes for lighting. This was the first official acceptance that electricity was now to be part of everyday life for every section of the community.

After D-Day in June 1944, most of the troops disappeared and life must have seemed rather quiet. At the end of the month a general fly-nuisance was reported across the country. The Urban Committee reported that it had sprayed 1,000 gallons of disinfectant on the town dump to preserve public health, and also that police efforts to keep stray dogs off the allotments seemed to have been a success.

In July Southern Command agreed to the removal of barbed wire defences along the main beach from Cobb Gate car park to the Cobb, and a Certificate of Merit presented to the borough by the National Allotments Society was framed and hung up in the Town Hall. In August, after 40 years' service, Town Crier Walter Abbott announced his retirement.

Autumn arrived and the Ministry of Home Security lifted blackout restrictions and, for the first time since 1939, limited street lighting was allowed. Mayor Emmett performed the switching on ceremony from the Malthouse. However, a proposal to improve street lighting by installing 'the new tube lamps' was rejected because the Highways Committee judged that 'ultra modern lighting would not be suitable for this Borough.'

The town's siren could once again be used as an ordinary fire-alarm, so the 'Old Fire bell' was returned to its place in the museum. Two evacuee families in the Gables, who were using candles instead of electric light because they said it was too expensive, were warned they faced eviction. And in January 1945 to save electricity the Highways Committee resolved that 'the public lights' be switched off on moonlit nights.

The Americans had not entirely disappeared. At New Year 1945 the council laid on a dance in the church hall for 'the entertainment of the US Army'. Each man was allowed to bring one partner, the council engaged the services of an American Service Dance Band, and had invitation cards printed with the Borough Arms and local views. The estimated cost of the party was £100. Clearly local feeling was that they rather liked their American visitors, and hoped to encourage them and their dollars to return as visitors after the war.

The end of the war was now in sight. At the end of January the Ministry of Health instructed the council to begin removing the pill-boxes, concrete cubes and other defences from the seafront and beaches. In March the council began to make plans for what were already referred to as VE Day celebrations. And in April, Town Clerk Atterbury reported that some troublesome evacuee families in the Gables, whom he had earlier failed to get the Mother Superior at Bridport Convent to accept, were going to be dealt with under the 'Evacuee Return to London Plan'.

FINAL CHAPTER

The council's plan for VE Day was for the official victory celebrations to take place in the evening. People would be asked to decorate the town with flags and bunting, the church bells would ring out and at 6.30pm the mayor and corporation would attend a religious service in the parish church. Then there would be a torchlight procession from Coram Court down to the Cobb, 'headed by Mr Williams' van'. As well as an electricians', and a wireless and cycle business in Coombe Street, Gordon Williams had a van with a loudspeaker on top. Through this, providing he drove carefully, gramophone records of the latest popular music could be played. With most of the Lyme Regis Silver Band still away in uniform, Mr Williams' van was the only – some might say also the preferable - mobile music on offer

Victory celebration speeches. A poor photo but it shows the town's dignitaries ranged on VE Day. Gordon Williams' van is on the left. Town Crier Walter Abbott is centre left clutching his mace. Mayor Emmett with chain stands centre.

The van would broadcast music for a floral dance which would follow behind the torchlight procession. A bonfire on the Cobb would light up the night and afterwards there would be a public dance on the Marine Parade, music again kindly supplied by Mr Williams and his van. And further to mark the occasion, the streetlights on VE Night would remain on until midnight, with extra lights placed along the Marine Parade. There was also a proposal for fairy lights in the Langmoor Gardens above until Town Clerk Atterbury reminded councillors that military regulations still in force stated 'no illuminations were allowed in this Area'. For the children the council proposed a Victory Tea.

As VE Day drew near the government became concerned that 'employees engaged in essential services' might, in order to participate in the long-awaited celebrations, desert their posts with the result that the entire national infrastructure would collapse. A stern circular from the Joint Industrial Council was sent to the Lyme Regis Electricity Committee emphasising the importance of ensuring that those on duty at the Malthouse resisted the temptation to join the fun. The council promised to pay them for VE Day at the full overtime rate, plus another day off in lieu.

By VE Day, preparations for changing Lyme over from its 440-volt DC to standard AC electricity from the national grid were well advanced. Detailed plans by Consulting Engineer Stewart for the changeover had been accepted in June 1944. These included the provision of three substations and drawings showing the layout of new overhead and underground mains throughout the town. All the existing 3-core DC mains cables would have to be replaced with new 4-core AC cables, but the wiring in individual houses could remain unchanged.

Stewart estimated that the changeover would cost £25,000 (perhaps £1.5m today) to be spread over five years. £15,000 would be for the initial work, mainly for the new substations and laying new mains at 9s. a yard (£0.50 a metre). The rest would go on extending the mains and promoting electricity sales. To justify this major investment it was vital that ordinary people now began to 'think electric'.

In January 1945 the council applied to the Electricity Commissioners to sanction the necessary loan. The Commissioners agreed subject to two conditions. First, they insisted that the council 'make the Electricity Undertaking one of its principal businesses', presumably to ensure the council kept electricity – and the loan repayments – high on its agenda.

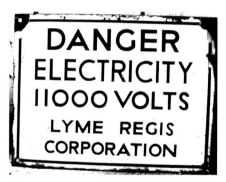

Secondly they specified that, after the changeover, a new electricity pricing-structure be introduced. In place of the old and, to our eyes, rather curious system of two different prices for the same electricity depending on whether you used it to light a lamp or boil a kettle, they wanted a single rate based on the size of your house and how much you used. Consumers would pay 1d per square foot (0.093 square metres) for their home's approximate floor area plus 3⁄4d per unit in summer and 1d per unit when it was cold and dark in winter. The expectation was that by cutting the cost of electricity for ordinary families in smaller homes, the council would 'increase the sales of electricity very considerably, especially for water-heaters, cookers and electric radiators'. From the consumer's point of view, only if you lived in a very large house lit mainly by candles were you likely to be worse off.

Finally, to promote electricity sales, the Commissioners suggested that the council follow Bridport's excellent example and set up its own Borough Electricity Showroom. This would show, hire out and with luck eventually lure the public into buying the latest electrical and electricity-hungry appliances. The council agreed.

However, the requisite £25,000 loan was considerable and needed justifying to the ratepayers. In February 1945 the council put out a statement. This explained that while it was in no way responsible for the Second World War or the 1942 explosion, its pre-war plans for electricity modernisation had necessarily been put on hold for the duration. The explosion had forced it to import AC power from the national grid, but converting this to suit the town's DC system and distributing it through the old mains 'involved a considerable loss of power'. The generators in the Malthouse still had to be run at peak periods, but these 'old oil engines installed in the early days are now, after good service, nearly at the end of their usefulness.' The statement then explained the scale of the works needed to change over to AC power direct from the national grid and ended, 'This expenditure is essential if a plentiful and cheap supply of electricity is to be provided, and whoever carries out the work, the cost must fall on the town.'

The first stage of the changeover was to carry out a house-by-house census of electrical appliances. Lights and heaters could be left as they were but anything with a motor – fridges, washing machines, etc – would need to be adapted to take the new 240-volt AC power. So would wireless sets unless they could be switched to either type of current. For adapting apparatus throughout the town the Committee finally budgeted 10s. per consumer. As the war ended Engineer Brown reported that the census was complete.

At the same time the council resolved to obtain premises for an electricity showroom and considered what to do about the consumers who were still paying off their connection costs through the Assisted Wiring Scheme. Their existing slot-meters, set at a slightly higher rate, would be obsolete when AC and the new two-part tariff came in. In their place the council proposed installing 'home-safes' to help families save up and pay off the loan.

In July 1945 came the general election with the landslide victory for Labour. Clement Attlee's government faced a grim prospect. If people had been expecting immediate fruits of victory they were to be disappointed. Three weeks after VE Day the Ministry of Food cut the rations for milk, bacon and cooking fat and for the first time introduced bread rationing, the one basic food that had managed to escape rationing all through the war.

There were shortages of virtually everything. American aid, which Britain had so relied upon, was now re-directed to reconstructing the ruins of continental Europe, and especially to starving Germany. By the end of 1945 council minutes were recording 'Food Gifts received from the people of the Dominions' – Canada, South Africa and Australia. And although in August the Electricity Committee had agreed to light the streets until 11pm, in September the Ministry of Power & Fuel wrote to the council stressing the importance of reducing lighting as much as possible to save fuel. It reverted to turning the streetlights off at ten, and on moonlit nights not lighting them at all.

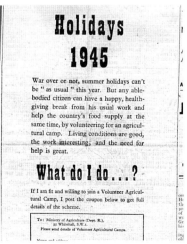

Bridport News, July 1945. Advertisement calling for volunteers for agricultural camps to help provide the nation's food supply.

Very gradually, however, life began to return to normal. Summer holidaymakers returned: receipts from bathing charges and deck-chairs for 1945 were £2,170 11s.6d compared with £1,291 12s.4d in 1943 and, despite continuing petrol rationing, car-parking receipts soared from just £2 5s.6d to £431 4s.0d. George's Square off Coombe Street, known for obvious reasons as 'Cats' Park', had been the site of an army cookhouse but in August 1945 it re-opened to the public. And men started coming back from the war. Charlie Camplin, who had joined up in 1940, was demobbed and re-instated in the Electricity Department in November, and Dick Hitchcock returned from the Royal Navy the following July.

In autumn 1945, the first phase of the work to change the town from DC to AC was put out to tender. Eight firms competed and in December the contract was awarded to Henley's Telegraphic Works Company with a quote of £5,144 4s.2d, the work to be completed in fifteen weeks. This phase consisted of bringing the AC supply up to a new main substation in the Langmoor Gardens and laying mains down either side of Broad Street. Consulting Engineer Stewart was engaged to visit the town at least once a month to inspect and measure the contractor's progress.

Arthur Brown had now been the borough electrical engineer since the end of the First World War. In November he announced that he would retire on 31st March 1946, and was then persuaded to delay to 30th June 30th . His successor, an electrical engineer from Bath called Warren Bradford, was appointed in February at a salary of £400 p.a. To start with, Bradford's role would be to supervise the DC/AC changeover as electrical clerk of works while Arthur continued in charge of the Malthouse and office. When Arthur retired Bradford would take over as borough electrical engineer.

Mr Bradford was given his own office in the new electricity showroom, the former fuel overseer's office in Church Street. At first he could find nowhere in the town to live so the council gave him permission to commute to work by motorbike from Exmouth, but it was made clear he was expected to reside in Lyme Regis from 1st July. The borough council's electrical engineer might be required at any hour of the night or day.

Recovering from the war - the Marine Parade in the late 1940s

Work should have started on phase one of the changeover in February 1946, but the 30 German prisoners of war promised to Henley's Telegraphic for labouring failed to appear and it was spring before work began. In late August, Henley's reported that they hoped to finish the first stage in a week, and on 30th September the chairman of the Electricity Committee proudly announced to the council that 'this afternoon certain properties in Lyme Regis have been connected to the AC supply' – presumably the shops and houses in Broad Street.

Now it was time to start increasing electricity sales. In the autumn the Electricity Committee agreed to offer cookers to residents through a hire purchase scheme. Engineer Bradford was authorised to buy six cookers, each complete with one kettle and two saucepans, to show off in his new electricity showroom. The Committee also resolved to apply to the Post Office Telephone Department for a telephone for his office, and to ask Messrs Bird & Sons of Birmingham to hold a series of electric cookery demonstrations in the Drill Hall over five days the following February. The chairman and Engineer Bradford would approach other manufacturers to see whether they would provide electrical appliances for display. To complete its electricity marketing campaign, the council authorised the purchase of a Ford 8 van at a cost of £189, plus £10 for a ladder rack on the roof and another £10 for painting and lettering it 'Lyme Regis Corporation Electricity Department'.

So it must have come as a bit of a shock when in November 1946 Councillor Frank Forrest drew his colleagues' attention to the fact that the King, in his speech at the Opening of Parliament, had announced Prime Minister Attlee's intention of nationalising their electricity department. The council chose to refer the matter to a meeting in committee (i.e. without the press) 'as this was a matter of major importance'. It certainly was: the estimated total cost of the changeover had just risen from £25,000 to £33,800.

Doodle by Prime Minister Clement Attlee.

1947 began with a famously hard winter. In March a gale brought down the grid lines between Dorchester and Bridport, cutting off the supply to Lyme. Engineer Bradford reported that the engines in the Malthouse, hardly used since the previous winter, had been put back into operation 'but immediately the light came on, consumers put on electric fires and it was necessary to cut off the supply on several occasions'. Naughty, naughty consumers. In fact in his report for the year to April 1947, Mr Bradford said that demand was up 35 per cent on the previous year. 775,860 units of old DC current and 109,834 units of the new AC current had been distributed. The second phase of the changeover would begin in June.

Ten German prisoners of war were engaged by Henley's that summer for phase two of the changeover. They, and 36 other PoWs allocated by the Ministry of Health to work on the post-war housing estate on Anning Road, arrived daily by coach from Bovingdon Camp near Dorchester. The task of the electricity department's PoWs was to hand-dig the trenches for new cables on either side of every street in town. The contractors paid the Ministry the union rate for the labour, although how much was passed on to the prisoners is not clear. In July, however, the Ministry of Health informed Henley's that on 15th August the prisoners would be withdrawn. 'Poles or other imported labour would be made available instead.'

Two years after the end of the war, the Germans were probably being sent home. In fact the Polish labour never appeared and Henley's used the labour shortage as an excuse to terminate its contract early. The real reason may have been that it had a difficult working relationship with Engineer Bradford. He now took over direct control of laying the remaining cables, employing local men as labourers as they were demobbed from the forces.

At about this time Mr Bradford instructed Junior Engineer Hitchcock to take all the old electricity records from Arthur Brown's former office in Electricity Cottage and burn them. These would probably have included records dating back to the early days of the private company before the First World War. Dick was no great admirer of Warren Bradford and, when he noticed various important looking documents among the papers including what appeared to be the deeds of the Malthouse, he thought, 'I'm not burning these', and hid a selection behind the main control panel indoors.

By October 1947 about a third of the town – 356 consumers – had been changed to the AC supply, and their various apparatuses converted. The only problems were with wireless sets. Many modern models could be switched to accept either AC or DC current, but local wireless engineers when making repairs often by-passed this facility with the result that when the set was connected to AC, it would unexpectedly burst into flames.

So did the Malthouse. *Pulman's Weekly* reported, 'Awaking on Wednesday morning to find that the electricity supply had failed, many consumers in Lyme Regis were then unaware that fire had destroyed the electricity station in Mill Lane, Coombe Street.'

The fire had started shortly after 10pm on 27th October, probably the result of old cables with perished insulation shorting out in the ceiling. Whatever the cause, Engineer Bradford had decided the 24-hour shift system was unnecessary so the Malthouse was unmanned.

Albert Boalch, living at the Mill House at the Town Mill across the yard, was now assistant borough surveyor as well as a member of the fire brigade. According to *Pulman's*, Albert had 'spotted smoke issuing from the electricity station. I raced down, telephoned the Fire Brigade, and called a shift engineer, Mr Dick Hitchcock. When we looked inside, the works were a mass of flames. We pulled out the fuses and made all we could "dead". The flames spread rapidly owing to the amount of oil in the building.'

'The cottages threatened by the fire were Electric Light Cottage, where Mr Richard Hitchcock, a shift engineer at the station, lives with his parents, and 5 Coombe Street, occupied by an elderly couple, Mr and Mrs T Stoodley.'

'Mrs Stoodley told our reporter, "We had gone to bed and were asleep when someone broke into our house, on police instructions, and told us that the electricity station was alight and to dress as hurriedly as possible. They broke a pane of glass in the sitting room and entered. We came downstairs and found the house full of people and our furniture being taken out into the street. We went to a neighbour's house and had a cup of tea. It was soon over. The police sergeant told us it was safe for us to return, and we went to bed again."'

The Malthouse roof and most of the generating equipment had been destroyed. So, ironically, had the documents Dick Hitchcock had so thoughtfully saved from the bonfire a few months before. Bradford and his staff worked solidly through the night and, as an emergency measure, fed the new AC supply into the old DC cables to provide power to those parts of the town still on DC. By the following afternoon much of Lyme had electricity once more.

The Malthouse the day after the fire. The three tanks in the foreground stored fuel-oil; those behind held river water to cool the engines. One of the infamous iron exhaust-chimneys from a silencing pit can be seen against the gable on the left.

Fire brigade volunteers (L to R) Donald Boalch, smoking builder Eli Emmett and Dennis Bowditch clearing up after the fire. The figure on the right is Tom Tabberer, the Department's head labourer. His father was Alban Woodroffe's gamekeeper.

Councillors were impressed by Junior Engineer Hitchcock's 'very courageous action in entering this burning building and your presence of mind in cutting off the high tension current'. Both the mayor and the town clerk wrote independently to thank him. Mayor King invited Dick to accept a small token of the council's appreciation – £10: more than twice his weekly wage – and hoped that he would have a happy Christmas. The council also resolved that 'the Ten Employees of the Undertaking who had worked so hard after the fire to provide a supply of electricity to all Consumers in the Town be each granted an Honorarium of Two Guineas' (£2 2s.0d).

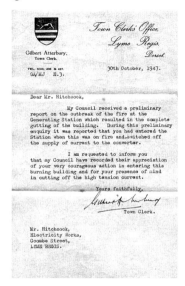

In fact the council could well afford to be generous. The Malthouse and its generating equipment were well insured. For 'damage to tools and machinery' – equipment which was virtually obsolete now that the national grid had arrived – it put in a claim for £5,358. And for fire damage to the Malthouse it claimed a further £7,058, bringing the total to well over £12,000. As a temporary measure it covered the burnt-out building with a corrugated iron roof. It is there to this day.

A mercury-arc rectifier of the type used in the final days of DC power.

To cope with the remaining but rapidly dwindling demand for DC power in the town, the council replaced the massive old motor converter with a mercury arc-rectifier, supplied by the Nevelin Electrical Equipment Co for £1,050. This bizarre Dr Frankenstein-type machine has no moving parts but a great glass bulb in which arcs of electric blue flash and crackled away, converting AC to DC power for the last few consumers.

As 1947 came to an end Rex Woodroffe, who had moved to the Argentine, wrote tendering his resignation from the council. It was accepted by his fellow councillors 'with regret'. They also voted to pay Mr Stratton £8 to re-wire the band's practice room at the Town Mill, this time with even a light for the stairs, and to send a telegram of congratulations to Princess Elizabeth on the occasion of her marriage to Lieutenant Philip Mountbatten.

The very last meeting of the Borough Electricity Committee was held on February 23rd 1948. It was not exciting. The Gilkes water-turbine and DC dynamo in the Town Mill were now redundant so they were sold to Messrs Christy Bros for £500 who wanted them for a farm in Cornwall. Engineer Rice was granted a shared telephone line to his home so he could be called out more easily, and Junior Engineer Hitchcock was promoted to Assistant Engineer, filling the shoes of Les Sharley who had moved on. But a cunning plan by the Committee to sell off its remaining stocks of fuel-oil before the government took them over was ruled by Town Clerk Atterbury to be illegal.

As nationalisation or 'Vesting Day' on 1st April 1948 approached, the awful realisation struck the council that the Government might take over not just the Malthouse but the entire Town Mill site. With spare parts and stores all over the place, they could argue that the whole group of buildings constituted the power station. There was a frantic rush to collect anything remotely electrical in the Mill and dump it firmly across the river in the Malthouse.

On 31st March 1948, the council held a celebration dinner at *The Three Cups Hotel* in Broad Street. The company of about forty included the Electricity Committee, the Department staff and distinguished guests. After the meal there were speeches.

For the South Western Area Electricity Board, from tomorrow the Malthouse staff's employers, the speaker was Councillor Frank Forrest, CBE. Frank, formerly a very senior engineer and manager with a large Midlands electricity undertaking, had retired to Lyme two years earlier, joined the council and also been appointed to the new Area Electricity Board. Lyme Regis could hardly have had a more distinguished electrical expert on its side.

Frank told the meeting that the future was bright and the time had now come for people 'to really use electricity and not play with it'. Of 35,000 farms and small-holdings in the south western area, only 20 per cent had electricity and only 8 per cent used it for any purpose other than lighting. 'It was not economical to run a half-mile line to supply a farmhouse that only wanted a few lights.' The object of the Board was to give a supply of electricity to every factory, farm, business and domestic premises in the areas at the lowest possible terms.

Then, reported *Pulman's Weekly News*, old Arthur Brown rose and spoke of the early days of the undertaking, started in 1909 and which he had served for 27 1/2 years. Finally, Mayor King gave the toast 'The Lyme Regis Electricity Undertaking. Officers and Staff, Present and Past'. The toast was acknowledged by Arthur Brown together with Miss Stoodley, typist to the Borough Electrical Engineer.

POSTSCRIPTS

1 Arthur Brown

The former borough electrical engineer died just before his 89th birthday in July 1960. His ashes were scattered on the East Cliff, from where Lyme Bay stretches away to Portland Bill.

Arthur Brown's obituary was the main story on the front page of the Lyme edition of The Bridport News. Headed, 'A Hero of "City of Blood" Dies in Lyme,' it told readers something of the 'adventure-packed life of one of Lyme's most interesting and colourful residents'.

Arthur was born on 24 July 1871 and grew up in Salford near Manchester. According to his birth certificate, his father Joseph's 'Rank or Profession' was 'A Market Gardener'. In those days mothers did not get ranks or professions, at least not on birth certificates.

Arthur joined the Royal Navy as an ordinary seaman in the days when sailors still wore straw hats and no shoes. He studied electrical engineering and at the age of 29 became one of the youngest in the Navy to reach the rank of warrant officer.

He saw active service in Africa and Asia and collected half a dozen medals. In 1897 he was part of the crew of *HMS Phoebe*, which sailed up the Niger and then cut through the jungle on a punitive expedition to the ancient city of Benin. With numerous reinforcements, they eventually reached the city, captured King Oba, confiscated his treasure and burnt much of Benin to the ground – thus 'the City of Blood'. Malaria, yellow fever and other disease caused many casualties and of the original *Phoebe* crew, only seven returned to England.

Arthur and Amy Brown on their wedding day.

Arthur married Amy in about 1900 and had two children, Arthur and Mildred, but continued serving as electrical engineer and torpedo gunner until the end of the First World War. After more than thirty years at sea he left the Navy in 1918 at the age of 47 and came to work for the Lyme Regis Electric Light & Power Company as its Resident Engineer.

Arthur and Amy's son Arthur also studied electrical engineering but then became a schoolmaster, first in Lyme Regis and later in Oxford. He then spent nearly 30 years as Commissioner of Scouts in Nigeria, retiring to the UK in the 1960s after Nigerian independence. Arthur and Amy's daughter Mildred married Joseph Humphries. Their grandson, Michael Humphries, is today a Fellow of the Institution of Electrical Engineers.

2 Money

I have not attempted to translate 'old money'– pounds, shillings and pence – into decimal currency. Values have changed so much since the move to decimal currency in 1971 that conversions are meaningless. Instead, I have tried to give other contemporary prices or wage-rates to compare against a particular value.

The chart below shows the changing value of £1 from 1908 to 1948; based on £1 in 2001. However, also note that prices have changed a great deal in relation to one another over the years. For instance, in 1937 a new Ford 'Popular' car cost £100 while the first Bendix automatic washing machine cost almost as much: £81. In 1911, a vacuum-cleaner cost the equivalent of several years' food shopping for a working family; by 2005 it was down to a few

What £1 in 2001 was worth between 1908 and 1948

Adapted from the House of Commons Library Research Paper 02/44 'The Value of the Pound 1750 - 2001'.

Based on House of Commons Library Research Paper 'The Value of the Pound 1750 – 2000'

days. The chart gives an average change in values; individual values will diverge greatly.

An interesting comparison appeared in Council records in November 1923, showing the wages in Lyme of the town clerk and a labourer before and after the First World War. (It was probably aimed at getting the town clerk a pay-rise.)

Labourer: 1914: 4d per hour   1920: 1s.4d per hour   1922: 1s. per hour.

Town Clerk: 1914: £100 per year 1920: £200 per year   1922: £200 per year

So for a 48-hour week in 1914, the Lyme Regis labourer got 16 shillings (£0.80p). The town clerk got just under £2 a week for a part-time job; he also had his solicitor's practice in Broad Street. After peaking at the beginning of the 1920s, wages and prices began to fall and did not recover until after the 1930s Depression.

Pounds, shillings and pence

Until the introduction of decimal currency, sterling was arranged in pounds, shillings and pence: £sd. There were 12 pence in a shilling and 20 in a pound, so there were 240 pence in a pound. The 'old money' was often written as follows:

A modern pound (left) = 100 pennies.
A 1914 pound (a gold sovereign) = 240 pennies (right)

£2 10s.0d (or £2-10-6d) is two pounds ten shillings (in decimal currency, £2.50).
5s. (or 5/-) is five shillings (in decimal currency, £0.25 or 25p.)
5s 6d(or 5/6d) is five shillings and sixpence.

Pocket money

These eight coins were in everyday use:

'Silver' coins were: sixpence (6d), shilling (1s. or 1/-), two shillings (2s. or 2/-), half a crown (2s.6d or 2/6d). 'Copper' coins: farthing (1/4d), half penny or 'ha'penny' (1/2d), penny (1d), three pence or 'thrupenny bit' (3d)

The gold sovereign (£1) and gold half sovereign worth 10s. (50p) were in circulation until 1931 when Britain abandoned the gold standard. The thrupenny bit (3d) first appeared in 1937 to replace a very small three-penny silver coin, unpopular because it so easily got lost.

Pricing conventions   Prices over £1 for goods in shops were often written just in shillings and pence, so you would commonly see 30s.(or 30/-.) instead of £1 10s.0d.   £3 5s.6d might well appear as 65s.6d or 65/6d.   Occasionally an archaic unit called a 'guinea' was used, meaning £1 1s.0d or 21/-.   Lawyers and doctors charged fees in guineas.

Bank notes   There were £5, £1 and 10s. (ten shilling) bank notes.

3 The old Borough Council

The principal source of information for the book has been the minutes of meetings of Lyme Regis Borough Council and its various committees – Urban, Highways, Cobb, Electricity, Bathing and so on.

Before local government re-organisation in 1974, the Borough Council really ruled the town. As well as the roads and harbour, parking, playgrounds and planning, council houses and the cemetery, it had for most of the century been responsible for public health and safety, water and sewerage, the fire brigade and the electricity supply.

The council usually comprised 16 members: the mayor, four aldermen and 11 councillors. There were four quarterly full council meetings, in February, May, August and November. Committees met more frequently, often almost monthly. The number of committees varied, but there were often eight or nine.

Over the years, council committees and their areas of responsibility were constantly changing in response to the needs of the town. Unless it is important, I have generally not specified which particular council committee originated a particular decision.

4 Electricity

'There's only two things you need to know about electricity, Martin,' said Phil-the-builder gloomily. 'You can't see it and it can kill you.' Phil was part of the restoration team at of the Town Mill.

His judgement pretty well sums up the popular view. From our earliest years we are told electricity is dangerous: 'Don't touch that.' 'Why?' 'You'll get electrocuted.' We are taught it is mysterious: 'What is electrocuted?' 'I don't know but it will really hurt, so do as you're told.' And we are constantly reminded it's expensive: 'Turn that light off.' 'Why?' 'Do you think we're made of money?'

So electricity has an image-problem; indeed, some might say that to write a book with 'electricity' in the title is taking a bit of a risk if the general plan is for people to buy it. Nevertheless, electricity is incredibly important stuff. We are now so dependent upon it that our civilisation would collapse within days without it. Therefore some basic understanding of it has got to be useful.

AC/DC

In an electric circuit, you can have either alternating current (AC) which flows along the wire in one direction and then the other, the direction alternating very quickly, or direct current (DC) which flows steadily in one direction. Both systems have their advantages, and when electricity first arrived, some supply companies installed AC systems and others DC. However, AC and DC do not mix, and much equipment designed to work with one sort will not work with the other.

A great advantage of DC, unlike AC, is that you can store it in batteries to use later. This useful property meant that, in the early days, many small towns as well as country houses, ships and farms successfully adopted DC systems.

AC, on the other hand, has the great advantage that you can transmit current over great distances very efficiently by transforming its voltage. That ability is what you need in order to develop a national grid. As DC does not transform easily, in the end it was the AC companies who won the argument and gradually the DC companies were forced to change.

The Nuts and Bolts of Watts and Volts

A watt is a measure of electrical power. The more watts, the more power. A 100-watt light bulb uses more power and gives more light than a 40-watt bulb. A kilowatt (kW) is a thousand watts. A 2kW electric heater uses twice as much power (and should be roughly twice as hot) as a 1kW heater.

To show how much electricity something uses, the manufacturers usually show the number of watts on the label. In fact the label should really say how many watts are used over an hour, e.g. 100 watts/hour, but as everyone knows this, manufacturers do not usually bother. Electricity bills usually charge for the number of units consumed. A Unit of electricity is one kilowatt used in one hour, often expressed as 1 kWh.

An amp or ampere measures the amount of electrical current. A volt measures electrical pressure or force. If you multiply amps by volts, you get watts. So 0.25 amps at 240 volts = 60 watts and 5 amps at 12 volts = 60 watts.

A good analogy is water. Think of amps as the diameter of a hose pipe and volts as the water pressure. Together, they will determine the amount of water squirting out of the end – the watts. Resistance, which is measured in ohms, is someone's foot on the pipe.

5 How this book came about

In early 2000 I found myself helping master millwright Martin Watts to rebuild the milling machinery and waterwheel at the Town Mill in Lyme Regis. Ours was the final phase in a long and costly project to rescue the derelict mill and return it to grinding corn.

Inside were the remains of a huge concrete tank, the rest of which had been recently cut out to make way for the new waterwheel we were going to build. Martin told me the tank had housed a water-turbine during the 1930s when the council used water-power to generate some of Lyme's electricity. Apparently in those days the council used to produce the town's electricity-supply. The water-turbine was for charging up batteries during the night, or something like that.

In spring 2001, after 75-years' silence, the mill was working again & an old man appeared. Dick Hitchcock said he had played in the mill as a child in the 1930s, and then been an apprentice in the council's generating station in the old Malthouse next door. 'You know, they'd send me to look outside at night, and if the moon was bright enough we'd turn the street-lamps off to save money.'

That was the hook. What a completely different way of looking at things from the way we look at them today. And what was all this about water-power and running a town on batteries? And Dick mentioned there had been an explosion.

Dick Hitchcock, left, with the author and the illustrator Ian Dicks (right)
in front of the Malthouse while researching the Electric Lyme exhibition in 2002

The following autumn Western Power Distribution agreed to sponsor a semi-permanent exhibition in the Town Mill about the history of the town's electricity supply. It would be called Electric Lyme. I would research it and the illustrator Ian Dicks would design it. Easy.

Only after the deal was done did we learn that most of the council's electricity records had been destroyed in a fire in 1947. Nobody we spoke to knew when the story of electricity in the town even began. 'Some time before the First World War, I think,' was the best they could do. So a paper-chase started in old newspaper archives in Taunton and Dorchester and at County Records Office. We more-or-less stumbled over the beginning. Then the picture began to grow.

In autumn 2003 the Electric Lyme exhibition opened. Its history had been wrung from sources from Cumbria to Kew. The picture that emerged of how our grandparents' generation lived and thought was fascinating. I was hooked. This book is the fruit of further research.

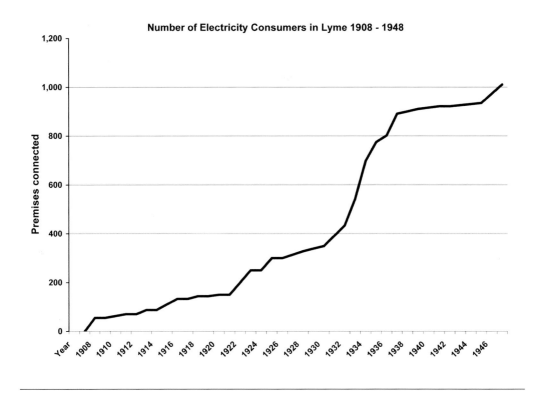

Number of Electricity Consumers in Lyme 1908 - 1948

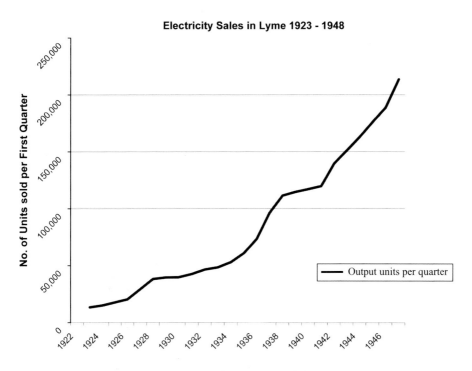

Electricity Sales in Lyme 1923 - 1948

Output units per quarter

Sales figures first appear when the council took over the undertaking. The rise in sales in the 1930s is less dramatic than the rise in consumer numbers because many of the new consumers had modest homes with just a few light bulbs.

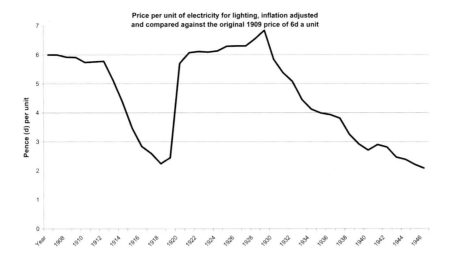

Price per unit of electricity for lighting, inflation adjusted and compared against the original 1909 price of 6d a unit

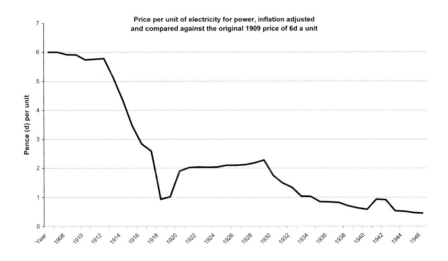

Price per unit of electricity for power, inflation adjusted and compared against the original 1909 price of 6d a unit

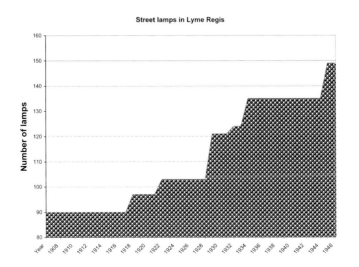

Street lamps in Lyme Regis

177

Mayors of Lyme Regis Borough Council
1900 - 1950

Henry Octavius Bickley	1900
John R C Talbot	1901
Samuel Harris	1903
George John Rendall	1904
James O'Neil	1906
Samuel Harris	1908
Alban Woodroffe	1910
Henry Octavius Bickley	1912
Alban J Woodroffe	1914
Alben Wiscombe	1919
Henry Ellis	1921
James Bragg	1924
George Frederick Eyre	1926
Reginald Walter Baker	1928
George H Worth	1932
George Frederick Eyre	1935
William J Emmett	1937
H I Blanchard	1945
Henry F King	1947

The Parish Church of St. Michael's
Lyme Regis – Vicars 1900 - 1950

William Jacob	1898
William Norman Willson	1915
Charles Carew Cox	1927
Geoffrey Lewis Tiarks	1954

INDEX